Healthy Cooking

G.I.

COOKBOOK

Healthy Cooking

G.I.
COOKBOOK

Paul Morgan

AN OCEANA BOOK

This edition published by Silverdale Books,
an imprint of Bookmart Ltd., in 2006

Bookmart Ltd.
Blaby Road
Wigston
Leicester
LE18 4SE

ISBN 10: 1-84509-236-8
ISBN 13: 978-1-84509-236-8

QUMHCGI

Manufactured in Singapore by
Pica Digital Pte. Ltd.
Printed in Singapore by
Star Standard Industries (Pte) Ltd

It is always sensible to consult your doctor before changing your diet
regime, but it is essential to do so if you suffer from any medical
condition or are taking medication of any kind. If you are concerned about
any symptoms that develop after changing your diet, consult your doctor
immediately. Information is given without any guarantees on the part of the
author and publisher, and they cannot be held responsible for the
contents of this book.

CONTENTS

INTRODUCTION

For 25 years or more, theories about what constitutes a healthy diet have chopped and changed. First, all fat was considered to be bad for you – then it was found that some types of fat can protect your heart. Then butter was considered bad, while margarine was thought to be good for you – but after a while, scientists discovered that margarine contained substances called trans fatty acids, which are extremely bad for you. At the same time, all cholesterol was once considered dangerous, but now we know that one type of cholesterol is, in fact, very good for you.

But while confusion reigned, one revolutionary concept remained relatively unknown. Called the glycaemic index, it was developed in 1981 by researchers at the University of Toronto, Canada, led by Dr David Jenkins, a professor of nutrition. Curiously, it did not come to public attention until 2002, when Professor Jennie-Brand Miller, of the University of Sydney, and others, wrote a book called *The New Glucose Revolution*. Within a short time, the idea of the glycaemic index, or 'GI', had taken the worlds of both nutrition and dieting – which had previously been very much at odds with each other – by storm.

It is now beyond dispute that by eating the glycaemic index way you can not only lose weight and maintain your weight loss – something that is very hard to do on fad diets – but improve your overall health and reduce the risks of developing high blood pressure, heart disease and diabetes. And as a bonus you will feel better, too, because a GI diet increases the levels of the feel-good chemical serotonin in the brain.

This book will show you how to achieve all this. First, we will look at the glycaemic index in detail and then show you how its use fits into an overall programme of healthy eating. Next, you can choose from a range of mouth-watering, healthy recipes. It may be a cliché, but like many clichés it is true: when it comes to your health, you really are what you eat!

Many salads have a low glycaemic index, but of course many of the dressings that can be bought these days do not. Try not to overindulge on these dressings.

A LITTLE OF WHAT YOU FANCY . . .

. . . may not, in fact, do you much good. But, unless your doctor has forbidden it, it is unlikely to do much harm, so long as it is just 'a little' and you do not indulge yourself often. As the recipes in this book show, a healthy diet can be a tasty diet, but, even so, eating completely healthy meals and snacks for seven days a week and 52 weeks a year can be a daunting prospect. So there is no point in worrying if you succumb to the urge to eat a packet of high GI pretzels or a greasy hamburger – but only do it very occasionally, as a special treat. Try to make sure that at least 90 per cent of your diet is healthy.

THE GLYCAEMIC INDEX AND CARBOHYDRATES

Carbohydrates are the body's primary source of fuel and are an essential part of a healthy diet. There are three types of carbohydrate: sugars, fibre and starch, and all of them are built from molecules of sugar. They used to be described as 'complex' or 'simple' carbohydrates, depending on whether they were simple forms of sugar or consisted of linked forms of sugar, and it was believed that simple carbohydrates should be avoided and complex ones preferred.

Today this categorization is now longer used. Instead, nutritionists classify carbohydrates according to their glycaemic index, or 'GI'. During the digestive process, carbohydrates are broken down into the simplest forms of sugar, and the glycaemic index measures how quickly this happens and so how fast levels of sugar in the blood rise – a high GI value means that the carbohydrate raises these levels very quickly indeed.

The significance of this is that the pancreas starts to produce the hormone insulin in response to rising blood sugar levels, and this promotes the uptake of sugar by the body's cells and reduces sugar levels in the blood. If you continually eat foods with a high GI – and if you have a hereditary disposition to the problem or are overweight and inactive – the levels of both insulin and sugar in your blood remain high, and you develop what is known as insulin resistance (the body loses its sensitivity to insulin, so more and more is needed). This can not only lead to type 2 diabetes, but result in high blood pressure, low levels of 'good' cholesterol (see page 11) and the risk of heart disease.

High or low?

In essence, whether a food has a high or low GI depends on how quickly its carbohydrates are converted to simple sugar during the digestive process. Foods that have not been processed – whole-grain foods – still contain their original fibre, which slows down the rate at which carbohydrates are converted to simple sugars and so also slows down the rate at which sugar enters the bloodstream; conversely, the carbohydrates in processed foods have already been partly broken down, meaning that their sugar enters the bloodstream relatively quickly.

However, the type of starch in the food is important, too: potatoes, for example, contain a starch that is broken down quickly during digestion. Other factors affecting the GI value are: ripeness – ripe fruit has a higher GI than unripe fruit; acidity – vinegar and

lemon juice delay stomach emptying and so reduce the GI value; and the size of food particles – small particles are more easily absorbed and increase the GI value.

PLUSES AND A MINUS

Maximizing the amount of low GI foods in your diet and minimizing the amount of high GI ones has numerous benefits:

● the slow breakdown of low GI foods during digestion and the gradual release of their sugars into your bloodstream means that you will not feel the 'sugar let-down' that comes when quick-release sugars are used up; in turn this means that you will not need to have another 'sugar hit' as quickly, so you will eat less – which means that you will lose weight (about 0.5 – 1 kg a week)

● the slow release of sugars into your bloodstream increases your physical endurance

● a low GI diet increases the body's sensitivity to insulin, which reduces the risk of developing insulin resistance, and so diabetes and heart disease

● including a larger proportion of low GI foods means that you will reduce your intake of 'bad' saturated fats and trans fats (see page 11) and lessen the likelihood that you will develop heart disease

● so long as you choose low GI foods, you can snack between meals

● a low GI diet leads to increased levels of serotonin in the brain – and serotonin makes you feel good.

A low GI diet can easily be followed for life, unlike other fad diets.

But, in case low GI diet seems too good to be true, there is just one minus:

● healthy though they may be, even low GI foods contain calories, so if you eat too many of them you will not lose weight: you still have to control portion sizes.

Fruit is one of the foods that has a low GI, and can be used as a starter and main course as well as for dessert.

Low-GI foods include soy, beans, fruit, milk and grainy bread; medium ones include sugar, orange juice and oats; while high-GI foods include potatoes, rice and wholemeal and white bread. It might seem a daunting prospect to exist solely on low-GI foods, but it is not necessary to do so. This is because eating a low-GI food reduces the GI value of high-GI foods when they are eaten at the same time – if, for example, you eat cornflakes (high GI) with milk (low GI) your blood sugar levels will not go up as quickly – what is known as the overall 'glycaemic load' (GL) is reduced. In essence, the equation reads:
'high GI + low GI = medium GI'
– so if you plan your menus carefully you can still eat some high-GI foods.

CHECK THE LABEL

Food manufacturers are starting to note GI values on product labels, and the practice is likely to become more and more widespread. (In fact, the World Health Authority advises that GI values should be stated and that the values for 'complex carbohydrates' and sugars, which are used currently, be dropped.) But how do you interpret the figures?

The answer is that the maximum GI value, which is based on pure glucose, is 100, and that foods are said to have a low GI when the value is 55 or less; to be medium GI when the value is between 56 and 69; and high GI when the value is 70 or more.

Remember that, ideally, you should stick to low GI foods; failing that, you should combine medium and low GI foods; and that if you ever eat high GI foods you should combine them with low GI ones.

FOODS TO CHOOSE
(Low glycaemic index carbohydrates)
Bran and porridge oats
Barley, buckwheat, and bulgar wheat
Some fruits – apples, citrus, berries, peaches, pears, plums and rhubarb
Pasta
Some vegetables – avocados, aubergine, beans (runner and green), broccoli, cabbage, cauliflower, carrots, celery, courgette, cucumber, leeks, onions, lettuce, mushrooms, olives, peas, peppers, spinach and tomatoes

FOODS TO AVOID
(High glycaemic index carbohydrates)
Breakfast cereals – cornflakes and sugar-coated cereals
White bread, cakes, biscuits, bagels, buns, muffins, pancakes and doughnuts
White and brown rice
Some fruits – dates, prunes and watermelon
Gnocchi
Some vegetables – broad beans, potatoes (when mashed, baked, fried or roasted), parsnips and swede
Sugar – table, glucose, treacle and molasses
Tomato ketchup

THE DANGERS OF BEING OVERWEIGHT

Being overweight brings with the dangers of many health problems, but if you carry the extra pounds on your waist – in the classic 'beer belly' – you are far more at risk of developing heart disease or diabetes. In fact, men with waists of more than 101 cm (40 in) and women with waists of more than 89 cm (35 in) are at between double and quadruple the risk of developing them.

The reason is that fat that is stored around the stomach secretes hormones that play havoc with the production of insulin, the pancreatic hormone that controls blood sugar levels. As a result 'insulin resistance' develops, leading to diabetes, high blood pressure and high cholesterol levels. And the healthiest and most effective way to lose weight is to follow the low GI diet.

YOUR DIET AND YOUR HEALTH

As we have seen, the low GI diet not only enables you to lose weight gradually and maintain your weight loss, but reduces the risk that you will develop insulin resistance and its accompanying problems. But this is a healthy eating cookbook, and the low GI diet is just one part of a healthy eating programme. It may address the problems caused by fast-sugar-release, high GI foods, but there are other, just as serious, problems that are founded in bad nutrition and can, largely, be avoided or, at the least, helped by a healthy diet. The most common of these is high blood pressure, which affects the whole circulatory system as well as the heart and atherosclerosis, affecting the arteries. Together and separately, they can lead to a heart attack or a stroke.

PRESSURE POINTS

The phrase 'high blood pressure' means that the force that blood exerts on the walls of arteries as it flows through them is higher than is normal. Blood pressure values are expressed as two figures, representing millimetres of mercury in an old-fashioned blood pressure measuring device (a sphygmomanometer): 120/80, for example, is considered normal – the first figure is the systolic pressure, when the heart is pumping; the second is the diastolic pressure, when the

White bread is a high GI food, so it is best not to overindulge on this. Wholewheat bread is medium to high GI.

heart is resting between beats. You are considered to have high blood pressure, and will be offered treatment for it, if your reading is 140/90 or higher. It is estimated that between 10 and 20 per cent of the population have high blood pressure, but many people do not know that they have it – there are often no symptoms, which is why it is sometimes known as 'the silent killer'. High blood pressure puts extra strain on the heart and over time weakens and damages arteries and veins.

Atherosclerosis is the condition in which plaques (atheromata) form on the inner walls of arteries. The plaques consist of dead cells, fibrous tissue and calcium, among other things, but primarily contain cholesterol. They can cause the arteries to harden, narrow and become less flexible (arteriosclerosis), or block them. If atherosclerosis blocks the coronary arteries, which supply the heart with blood, the result will be a heart attack. Sometimes, too, pieces of plaque can break off (thrombi) and be carried around the circulatory system to block other, smaller blood vessels – if these supply blood to the brain, the result could be a stroke.

The nature of the link between atherosclerosis and high blood pressure is complex. Each condition can cause the other one, but generally both develop as a result of lifestyle factors and the natural processes of ageing (some people also have an inherited predisposition to them). Smoking, drinking excessive amounts of alcohol, obesity, high stress levels and the presence of other conditions, such as diabetes, play a major part in the development of both problems, but so, too, does your diet.

THE CULPRITS

The main dietary culprits when it comes to developing atherosclerosis and high blood pressure are saturated fats, trans fats, dietary cholesterol and salt. But some foods can actually prevent both problems. The trick is to know which foods to choose and which to avoid – and what follows will show you. Remember, too, that the more low GI foods you include in your diet, the less likely it is that you will eat 'bad' fats (see page 11).

You should try to avoid foods containing high sugar and fat content, such as crisps, chips, cakes, pastries and ice-cream.

KEEP CHECKING

There are often no symptoms if you have high blood pressure – which is why it is known as 'the silent killer'. But it is important that you know what your blood pressure is, so that you can take steps to reduce it if it is too high. In Britain, it is recommended that everybody asks their family doctor to check their blood pressure every five years, and more frequently with age; in the US, the recommendation is that blood pressure should be checked every two years over the age of 20.

You can buy blood pressure monitors for home use, and a wide range of them is available on the internet. However, you should make sure to choose a model whose results have been validated by medical associations, because some models can give inaccurate results.

BLOOD LEVELS

If your blood pressure is too high, a blood sample may be taken so that it can be tested for levels of cholesterol and tryglycerides (the form in which fats are transported in the blood). Depending on the result, you may be advised to adopt healthy eating measures and in some cases may be prescribed statin drugs, which control cholesterol levels.

FATS AND CHOLESTEROL

For many years, scientists believed that the cholesterol that you eat is the villain of the piece when it comes to heart disease. In fact, about 75 per cent of the cholesterol in your blood is manufactured by your liver, while only 25 per cent of it is in your diet. And the liver uses dietary fat to make cholesterol. When this was appreciated, the emphasis moved to eating a low-fat and low-cholesterol diet. But then it was discovered that it is not only the amount of fat in your diet that is important, but how much of which type of fat you eat – and there are three main types of fat: saturated fats, unsaturated fats and trans fats.

Saturated fats are found in meat, poultry, lard and whole-milk dairy products, such as cheese, milk, butter and cream, but high levels are also found in some vegetable oils, such as coconut and palm oil.

Unsaturated fats, which typically are liquid at room temperature, are found in plant and vegetable oils, such as olive, peanut, sesame, safflower, corn, sunflower, canola and soybean oil, and in avocados, oily fish (in the form of omega–3 fatty acid), and nuts and seeds.

Trans fats are man-made – a by-product of heating vegetable oils in the presence of hydrogen (which is why they are often referred to as 'hydrogenated vegetable oils' on product labels). They are found in commercially baked goods, such as biscuits, snack foods, processed foods and commercially prepared fried foods, such as crisps. Some margarines also contain high levels of trans fats, especially brands that are 'stick' margarines – spreadable ones have less high levels as they are less hydrogenated (hydrogenation makes the fat hard at room temperature).

Where cholesterol comes in

Your body needs cholesterol to function correctly – it is involved in the production of hormones, the body's chemical messengers, as well as bile and vitamin D, and is found in every part of the body. For this reason, it is manufactured in the liver – and the liver uses fats to make it. If you eat too much saturated fat, the liver produces too much cholesterol. And, unfortunately, cholesterol is a soft, waxy substance that can stick to the lining of blood vessels and obstruct them if there are high levels of it in the blood.

Peanuts are a good snack food, as they contain no cholesterol and are high in unsaturated fat.

As we have seen, liver-produced cholesterol, and so the cholesterol that is ultimately the result of fat consumption, accounts for around 75 per cent of the cholesterol found in you blood. The remaining 25 per cent comes from the cholesterol you eat. Dietary cholesterol is found in eggs, dairy products, meat, poultry, fish and shellfish, but the highest levels are found in egg yolks, meats such as liver and kidneys and shellfish. Vegetables, fruits, nuts, grains and cereals contain no cholesterol.

'Good' and 'bad' cholesterol

Cholesterol is carried around the body by chemicals called lipoproteins. There are two types: low-density lipoprotein (LDL) and high-density lipoprotein (HDL). If there is too much of the cholesterol carried by LDL, known as 'bad' cholesterol, plaque builds up on arterial walls. But HDL carries cholesterol away from the arteries to the liver, which breaks it down so that it can be excreted from the body; for this reason, HDL cholesterol is said to be 'good' cholesterol.

For some years, scientists have known that saturated fats, and, in particular, trans fats, increase the blood levels of harmful LDL cholesterol and lower levels of beneficial HDL cholesterol, while unsaturated fats have the opposite effect. In January 2005, however, researchers at the Dana-Farber Cancer Institute, in the US, reported that they had discovered the mechanism responsible. It appears that saturated fats trigger a biochemical activator in the liver that boosts LDL cholesterol production.

To sum up, then, a healthy heart diet is one that has low levels of saturated and trans fats, and high levels of unsaturated fats.

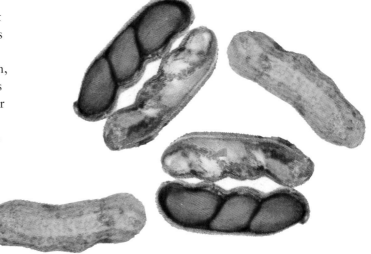

FOODS TO CHOOSE

(Containing unsaturated fat)

Vegetable oils – pure olive, peanut, walnut, sesame, corn, soybean, sunflower and safflower oils

Avocados

Oily fish – salmon, mackerel, tuna, herrings and so on

Nuts and *seeds*

Spreadable, unsaturated margarine

FOODS TO USE SPARINGLY

(Containing saturated fat)

Whole-fat milk (skimmed milk is preferable)

Butter, cream, cheese, full-fat yoghurt (low-fat is preferable), *ice cream*

Meat – beef, lamb and pork

Poultry – battery-farmed chicken (free-range is preferable), goose, duck and turkey (wild game, such as rabbit, wild duck and venison is better)

Lard

Eggs (especially ones from battery-farmed chickens)

Coconut oil and *palm oil*

FOODS TO AVOID

(Containing trans fats)

Ready-made commercial foods – cakes, biscuits and snack foods

Processed foods – sausages, pâté, scotch eggs, pies and so on

Commercially prepared fried foods – crisps, battered fish and chips

Hard margarine

FOODS TO USE SPARINGLY

(Rich in dietary cholesterol)

Organ meats – liver and kidneys

Eggs (especially ones from battery-farmed chickens)

Shellfish

Red meat

A FAMILY INHERITANCE

If members of your family suffered heart attacks at an early age – in their 40s or 50s – you may have inherited a condition called hypercholesterolaemia, in which a genetic mutation causes extremely high levels of LDL cholesterol in the blood. It is vital that you consult your doctor if you have such family associations, because if you have inherited the faulty gene you have an 85 per cent chance of suffering a heart attack before the age of 60. You are more likely to suffer from hypercholesterolaemia if you come from one of these populations (in increasing order of likelihood: French Canadians from Quebec; Lebanese Christians; Afrikaners; and Ashkenazi Jews.

It is vital that sufferers adopt strict dietary measures to control their blood cholesterol measures, and statin drugs are often given to help reduce blood levels.

Eggs are full of nutrients, proteins, vitamins and minerals, but must be eaten in moderation as very high levels of cholesterol are found in the egg yolk.

SALT

The more salt you eat, the more your body retains fluid, and the more fluid there is, the harder your heart has to work to pump blood around your body. And the result of this increase in the heart's work rate is high blood pressure and the risk, over time, of developing heart failure. Some groups of people are said to be 'salt sensitive', and are at particular risk of heart damage even without a rise in blood pressure. They include people with diabetes, the elderly and people of Afro-Caribbean origin.

Doctors recommend that our daily intake of salt should be less than 6 grams – about a teaspoonful. Even less salt than this is recommended for those who already have heart problems. The level is lower for children, too up to 6 months old, it is less than 1 gram; between 7 and 12 months it is 1 gram; between 1 and 3 years it is 2 grams; between 4 and 6 it is 3 grams; and between 7 and 10 years it is 5 grams. Worryingly, one small can of spaghetti hoops served on a piece of toast made from white, supermarket bread contains around 0.9 grams – half of a toddler's recommended daily intake.

Hidden salt

The 6 gram target sounds an easy enough one to achieve, but in fact it is very tall order. The reason is that this target refers to our total salt intake, not just to the salt that we add to our food, and there is a considerable amount of salt hidden in the foods many of us eat. Processed foods are mainly to blame – in fact, researchers estimate that around 75 per cent of our salt intake comes from them.

It is obvious that some foods contain high salt levels salted nuts, crisps, olives and anchovies, for example, all taste, and are, salty. But bacon, cheese, pickles, stock cubes, sausages and smoked meat and fish contain salt, too. And some brands of biscuits, pizzas, 'ready meals', soups and breakfast cereals are also surprisingly high in salt.

The only way to check which processed foods are high in salt is to read product labels carefully. It is easy to come unstuck when you do this, however, because some labels do not refer to the product's salt content but to its sodium content (salt is made up of sodium and chloride). The two values are not the same – in fact, you have to multiply the sodium value by 2.5 to obtain the real salt content.

Reducing your salt intake

If you cut down on salt, your blood pressure will fall within weeks, even if it was not too high in the first place. And that means that your risk of developing heart disease or having a stroke will also fall.

Many people think that their food will lack taste if they cut down on salt, but this is a myth. You may find that your diet is a little bland for the first week or so, but your taste buds soon adapt. Adopt these salt reduction strategies and you will find the process much more easy.

- Avoid processed foods
- Check the salt levels of all commercially prepared foods, including everyday products such as bread
- Throw away your salt shaker
- Make your own salt-free stocks and sauces
- Use alternative seasonings, such as lemon juice, herbs and vinegar
- Eat fresh fruit (bananas and avocados in particular) and vegetables the potassium they contain helps counter the effect of dietary salt
- Do not switch to sea salt, rock salt or garlic salt – they are not different to normal salt
- Ask your doctor whether salt substitutes are suitable for you.

FOODS TO AVOID

All types of salt – table, rock, sea and garlic
Obviously salty foods – anchovies, salted nuts, ready-salted crisps

FOODS TO USE SPARINGLY

(High in salt)
Commercially made foods – biscuits, supermarket bread, cheese biscuits and crisps
Ready-made meals – including pasta, pizzas, curries and Asian cuisine
Tinned foods – baked beans, spaghetti, meats and vegetables
Preserved and smoked foods – bacon, ham, pickles, spiced sausage, stock cubes and sauces

---

CALCULATE YOUR SALT INTAKE

If you must eat processed foods – and it can be hard not to – try to make sure that you stay within the recommended daily intake of 6 grams of salt. Read a product's label to find the number of grams of salt in 100 grams of the contents. If the quantity of sodium is given, multiply by 2.5 to calculate the actual salt content. (If the value is given in milligrams, or 'mg', divide by 1,000 to convert it to grams.)

Then look for the total weight of the contents, or estimate the proportion of them that you intend to use. Divide the weight that you will use by 100, then multiply by the number of grams of salt in each 100 grams and you will discover how much salt you will eat. The results can be surprising: one small (200 g) can of baked beans can contain as much as 1.7 grams of salt – just under a third of your total recommended intake; one slice of white, refined bread contains 0.61 grams of salt – so just the bread making up a lunchtime sandwich could well account for just under a fifth of your total recommended daily intake.

Advacado is very rich in potassium, which helps counteract the effect of too much salt.

SALT SUBSTITUTES

Some people find that their food tastes a little bland when they switch to a low-salt diet, and even though their taste buds will adapt within a few weeks some people find that they need a little help to make the change. A number of salt substitutes are on the market, but these contain part sodium and part potassium and in certain circumstances it is possible to overload your body with potassium – consult your doctor before using a commercial salt substitute.

Make your own

This recipe for a salt substitute relies on the principle that a sour flavour is a good substitute for a salty one. It uses the grapefruit peel (or lemon or orange peel, for a weaker taste) and citric acid crystal. Also known as 'sour salt' and 'lemon salt', these can be found in the baking section of supermarkets or in delicatessens.

Ingredients
- the peel of 1 grapefruit
- 1 tbsp ground allspice
- ½ tbsp citric acid crystals

Makes 3 tablespoons

Method

1 Peel the grapefruit as thinly as possible, then scrape away all the white parts. Dry the peel overnight near a source of heat.

2 Grind the dried peel in a coffee grinder or spice grinder, then combine it with the other ingredients. Put the mixture into a well-sealed bottle and shake well to mix. Store in a dry place.

Variations

Add a tablespoon of freshly ground black pepper to the mixture to make it into citrus pepper, an ideal seasoning for meat.

Free-range chicken eggs provide a good source of protein, and as well as using these in the recipes in this book, they can also be used on their own, poached, boiled and scrambled, to name just a few ways to serve them.

Protective protein?

Scientists have theorized that eating large amounts of protein might have beneficial effects on the cardiovascular system, but the question has not yet been resolved. However, one large-scale, 14-year study – the Nurses' Health Study, in the US – showed that women who ate about 110 grams of protein a day were 25 per cent less likely to suffer from heart problems than women who ate 68 grams a day; whether the protein came from animal or vegetable sources did not matter, and nor did the fat levels in the women's diet. So there are certainly no dangers to eating relatively large amounts of protein, though preferably from sources that do not contain saturated fats, and there may be a beneficial effect.

One protein that has definitively been shown to help prevent heart disease by lowering cholesterol levels is soy. An analysis of 38 different trials has shown that eating 50 grams of soy protein a day instead of animal protein lowered LDL cholesterol levels by 12.9 per cent – a significant figure.

PROTEIN

Protein, made up from chemicals called amino acids, makes up the building blocks of all our body's tissues except stored fat. You need to eat a certain amount of protein every day – a minimum of one gram for every kilogram of body weight – to prevent the body from starting to break down tissue. And you need more than that if you want to build up healthy muscles and robust bones.

It is easy to get enough protein in your diet in Western industrialized societies, though hard to do so in developing countries. But the quantity of protein you eat is not the whole story. What is important is that you eat a variety of amino acids, which means protein from a variety of sources. This does not mean that it is essential to eat steaks, for example, because you can obtain a full range of proteins from vegetable and fruit sources, if you are a vegetarian. Variety is the spice of life – and in this case it is also healthy!

FOODS TO CHOOSE

('Good' protein – lower in saturated fats)
Vegetables – beans, brown rice, lentils, millet and pulses
Soybeans
Nuts – brazil, peanuts and pine-nuts
Seeds – sesame
Free-range chicken and turkey (but remove the skin)
Locally sourced lean cuts of non-intensively reared meats – beef, lamb, pork and veal
Free-range chicken eggs (but not duck or goose eggs)

FIBRE

Our bodies cannot digest some of the food that we eat, and it is this indigestible material that is known as dietary fibre. Most people know that a diet high in fibre is good for your bowel function and can protect against disorders of the intestines, such as cancer of the colon, but it is less well known that fibre can also lower the levels of cholesterol in your blood.

There are two types of fibre insoluble and soluble (the latter is so-called because it forms a gel when mixed with liquid). Insoluble fibre plays the main part in promoting bowel function, and high levels of it are found in foods such as whole-wheat bread, wheat cereals, rice, barley, grains, cabbage, carrots and so on. But it is soluble fibre that reduces blood cholesterol – though it is not clear how it does this. It is found in oats, oat bran, oatmeal, peas, beans, barley and fruits, and, conveniently, foods containing soluble fibre have a low GI rating.

Five a day

So it makes sense to increase your intake of foods rich in fibre, and especially of those rich in soluble fibre – generally, it is recommended that you should eat five portions of fibre-rich fruit and vegetables a day. And, of course, foods such as these are low in saturated fats and cholesterol. Make sure that you read labels very carefully, though, because some commercial products that claim to be rich in fibre in fact contain very little of it.

Pulses such as lentils and split peas and oats are all high in soluble fibre. This type of fibre has a low GI rating, and can also lower the blood cholesterol levels.

FOODS TO CHOOSE
(High in soluble fibre)
Oatmeal and oat bran
Lentils, beans and peas
Apples, bananas, blueberries, oranges, pears and strawberries
Sweetcorn, spinach, spring greens and broccoli
Nuts –almonds, brazil, hazel, peanuts, pecan, pistachio, walnuts
Seeds – sesame, sunflower and pumpkin

FOODS TO USE
(High in insoluble fibre)
Whole grains – bran, wheat, couscous, brown rice, bulgur and barley
Wholemeal and granary bread
Wholemeal pasta
Wholemeal flour
Whole-grain breakfast cereals
Fruit – both fresh and dried
All vegetables – but especially brussel sprouts, carrots, cabbage, okra, parsnips, sweetcorn, courgettes, cucumber, celery, tomatoes and unpeeled potatoes

VITAMINS, MINERALS AND ANTIOXIDANTS

There is absolutely no doubt that every one of our body's systems needs vitamins and minerals to function. Vitamins act as catalysts, initiating and controlling chemical reactions in the body. Only small amounts of them are needed – they are known as micronutrients – and they must be obtained from our diet, because the body cannot manufacture them. If you follow the rules for healthy eating given in this book, and take a multivitamin supplement every day, as a precaution, you should absorb all the vitamins and minerals that your body requires. But sometimes the way that we treat and cook food reduces its content of micronutrients. Follow these rules to make sure that you can meet your body's requirements.

● Avoid processed foods, and canned foods in particular, because these can be low in vitamin content.

● Always use fresh or frozen fruit and vegetables, because vitamin levels decrease as these foods age. It is not generally realised that freezing preserves vitamin content, but chilling fruit and vegetables in a refrigerator before heating them can reduce levels of vitamins such as vitamin C and folic acid by up to 30 per cent. Remember that frozen vegetables – peas, especially – are often more vitamin-rich than fresh ones, because they are frozen immediately after being picked.

● Keep all foods away from heat, light and air, all of which reduce levels of vitamin C and the B vitamins.

● Store vegetables in airtight bags.

● Use the skin of fruits and vegetables wherever possible and avoid trimming them too much. Instead of peeling, wash or scrub the – most of the nutritional value of fruits and vegetables is contained in the skin or the area underneath it.

● Keep the water you have used to cook vegetables and use it as a base for stock or sauces – otherwise you will lose the valuable vitamins and minerals that have leached into the water.

Instead of peeling, the skin of fruit and vegetables should be scrubbed and left on if possible, as most of the vitamins and nutrients are just below the skins.

● Take a daily multivitamin supplement – it can be hard to obtain sufficient quantities of some vitamins, such as B12 and folic acid from your diet; and fibre-rich foods contain chemicals called phytates, which can bind with some minerals and interfere with their absorption. But think of it as a nutritional safety net, rather than as a substitute for healthy eating.

HOMOCYSTEINE

Some research has linked high levels of a protein called homocysteine in the blood with high levels of the 'bad' LDL cholesterol. The theory is that homocysteine changes cholesterol into this 'bad' form. Normally, homocysteine is broken down to form new proteins for the body with the help of vitamins B6 and B12 and folic acid, and the theory is that people with high homocysteine levels lack sufficient of these vitamins in their diet.

Research has yet to confirm this theory, though several studies are ongoing and more should be known soon. Until the results are in, however, it would be sensible to make sure that you eat sufficient vitamin B6 and B12 and folic acid in your diet. Foods rich in them include asparagus, avocados, bananas, beans, cabbage, carrots, fish, lentils and spinach, and – though these should be eaten sparingly – cheese, milk, beef, yoghurt and eggs.

ANTIOXIDANTS

Many of our bodily structures can be damaged by the presence of what are known as 'free radicals' – technically speaking, these are atoms that have unpaired electrons. The most common free radical is radical oxygen, which can damage cells and increase the likelihood that LDL 'bad' cholesterol forms fatty plaques in arteries.

When this was realised, in the 1990s, nutritionists started to look at the antioxidants, which combat radical oxygen – the most common ones being vitamins C and E and beta-carotene (a precursor to vitamin A) and lycopene. Soon antioxidant supplements became increasingly popular, and today some 30 per cent of Americans take them. Unfortunately, they do not have reduce the risks of heart disease or stroke, as a series of studies, and meta-studies (that is, studies of studies) have shown.

Nevertheless, it has been shown that a diet that is high in antioxidants is protective against heart disease.

The answer to this conundrum is thought to be that in practice the effect of dietary antioxidants relies on the interaction between the antioxidants and other dietary ingredients minerals, perhaps, or fibre. So it is important to eat a diet rich in antioxidants – that means richly coloured fruit and vegetables that contain chemicals called flavonoids, such as apricots, blueberries, bilberries, broccoli, carrots, mangos, peppers and spinach, and, in particular, tomatoes (though these should be cooked to release maximum quantities of flavonoids). And, just to show that a

A fresh vegetable salad is far more beneficial in terms of nutritional value than cooked vegetables, and peppers contain more vitamin C than oranges. They also look very colourful in salads.

healthy heart diet need not be without its luxuries, there are high levels of flavonoids in both dark chocolate and red wine – though both should be enjoyed in moderation.

TOO MUCH CAN BE DANGEROUS

Many people take high doses of vitamin supplements, without having taken medical advice. But doing so can be dangerous, because in many cases the effects of high doses are not known, and in some cases the effects have been confirmed to be dangerous. For example, it was once thought that very high doses of vitamin E might help prevent heart disease, but several studies have failed to show this and a recent study suggests that they may make heart failure more likely. And the list goes on: too much calcium can lead to lethargy, confusion and coma; excess vitamin B6 can cause a nerve disorder that leads to loss of feeling in the arms and legs; high doses of vitamin A can increase the risk of cardiovascular disease and can damage your liver; excessive doses of vitamin C can cause abdominal pain, nausea and diarrhoea; and so on.

The message is clear: do not take high-dose vitamin supplements unless they have been prescribed by your doctor – you can obtain all the vitamins and minerals you need by eating a healthy diet and taking a daily multivitamin supplement.

VITAMIN– AND MINERAL-RICH FOODS

(NB Pre-menopausal women and women taking HRT should eat more of foods containing vitamins that are depleted by the female hormone oestrogen.)

Vitamin A (antioxidant)
Retinol: butter, cod liver oil and cheese
Beta-carotene: apricots, cantaloupe, carrots, kale, peach, peas, spinach and sweet potatoes

Vitamin B1
Beans, brown rice, milk, oatmeal, vegetables, whole grains and yeast (depleted by alcohol, caffeine, exposure to air and water, food additives and oestrogen)

Vitamin B2
Eggs, fish, meat, milk, vegetables and whole grains (depleted by alcohol, caffeine, oestrogen and zinc)

Vitamin B3
Avocado, eggs, fish, meat, peanuts, prunes, seeds and whole grains (destroyed by canning and some sleeping pills; depleted by alcohol and oestrogen)

Vitamin B5
Bran, eggs, green vegetables, meat, whole grains and yeast (destroyed by canning)

Vitamin B6
Avocado, bananas, cabbage, cantaloupe, fish, milk, eggs, seeds and wheat bran (destroyed by alcohol, heat, oestrogen and processing techniques during production of commercial food)

Vitamin B folic acid
Apricots, avocados, beans, carrots, green vegetables, melons, oranges and whole wheat (destroyed by commercial food processing techniques, cooking and exposure to water and air, depleted by alcohol)

Vitamin B12
Dairy products, fish and meat (depleted by alcohol, exposure to sunlight and water, oestrogen and sleeping tablets)

Vitamin C (antioxidant)
Broccoli, cabbage, cauliflower, citrus fruits, green peppers, spinach, tomatoes and potatoes (destroyed by boiling, exposure to air, and carbon dioxide and long storage; depleted by alcohol, aspirin, oestrogen, stress and tobacco)

Vitamin D
Cod liver oil, dairy products and oily fish (depleted by lack of sunlight)

Vitamin E (antioxidant)
Almonds, broccoli, eggs, kale, oats, olive oil, peanuts, soybeans, seeds, spinach and wheat germ (destroyed by commercial food processing techniques, freezing, heat, oxygen and chlorine; depleted by smoking and use of contraceptive pills)

Vitamin K
Broccoli, cod liver oil, eggs, green vegetables, live yoghurt, tomatoes and whole grains

Magnesium
Bitter chocolate, brown rice, nuts, soybeans and whole wheat (depleted by caffeine and stress)

Zinc (antioxidant)
Eggs, meat, mushrooms, yeast and whole grains (inhibited by caffeine and smoking)

Potassium
Avocados, bananas, dried fruit, green vegetables, nuts and potatoes (lost in diarrhoea and sweat)

Selenium (antioxidant)
Broccoli, onions, tomatoes, tuna and wheat germ

STRIKING A BALANCE

It is easy to decide which foods you should eat, but more difficult to decide how often to eat them. It is also hard to strike a nutritional balance between foods so that you obtain all the nutrients that your body demands in the correct quantities, yet protect yourself from eating too much of the potentially harmful food groups. And you will have noticed already from the tables in this book that certain foods are 'good' in the sense that they contain substantial quantities of a desirable ingredient, but 'not so good' in that they contain less desirable ingredients. So how do you do it?

The healthy eating pyramid shown on the opposite page indicates how often you should eat the different food groups. For instance, while foods such as cheese and other dairy products are important to eat as part of a balanced diet, you should try to use these sparingly because of the high levels of saturated fat they contain.

It combines sound nutritional advice with common sense. Use it to help plan your GI diet and for general good health.

EXPLAINING THE SYMBOLS

SOLUBLE FIBRE

 HIGH

 MEDIUM

 LOW

PROTEIN

 HIGH

 MEDIUM

 LOW

ANTIOXIDANT

 HIGH

 MEDIUM

LOW

SATURATED FAT

 HIGH

 MEDIUM

 LOW

UNSATURATED FAT

 HIGH

 MEDIUM

LOW

CHOLESTEROL

 HIGH

 MEDIUM

LOW

GLYCAEMIC INDEX

 HIGH

 MEDIUM

 LOW

INSOLUBLE FIBRE

 HIGH

 MEDIUM

LOW

HEALTHY EATING PYRAMID

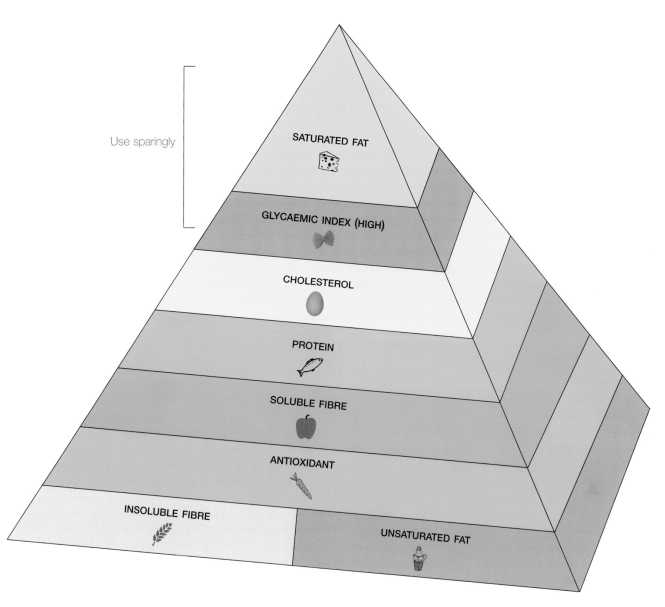

Use sparingly

SATURATED FAT

GLYCAEMIC INDEX (HIGH)

CHOLESTEROL

PROTEIN

SOLUBLE FIBRE

ANTIOXIDANT

INSOLUBLE FIBRE

UNSATURATED FAT

 Saturated Fat: Red meat, goose, duck, cheese, butter, cream, full-fat yoghurt

 Glycaemic Index (HIGH): Rice, white bread, potatoes, desserts, broad beans, prunes, watermelon, and pasta

 Cholesterol: Eggs, butter, cream, cheese, shellfish, pork, lamb, beef (0–1 times daily)

 Protein: Fish, shellfish, free-range chicken, rabbit, wild game, low-fat dairy (1–2 times daily)

 Soluble Fibre: Oats, barley, peas, beans, fruits (e.g. apples, oranges, bananas) nuts (2–3 times daily)

 Antioxidant: Spinach, broccoli, garlic, onions, red and orange vegetables and fruit, berries (at most meals)

 Insoluble Fibre: Wheat bran, wholemeal flour, wild rice, grains, cabbage, cauliflower, fruit skins (at most meals)

 Unsaturated Fat: Olive oil, soya beans, avocado, peanuts, salmon, mackerel, tuna, sardines (1–2 times daily)

HOW TO COOK HEALTHILY

There is little point in choosing healthy heart ingredients and recipes if you cook them in a way that is in itself unhealthy. For diabetics in particular it is important to choose cooking methods that not only help reduce cholesterol and saturated fats, so reducing the risk of heart disease, and to keep the calorie count low, but maximize the nutritional value of each dish. These techniques are effective, but may require a little practice:

- Baking – good for vegetables, fruit, poultry and lean meat, as well as for puddings; you may need a little extra liquid

- Braising or stewing – brown first, on top of the stove, then cook in a small quantity of liquid; if you leave the dish in a refrigerator you can remove the chilled fat and then reheat it

- Grilling – on a rack, so that fat can drain away

- Microwaving – place the food between two paper towels to drain fat away while it cooks

- Poaching – in a covered pan of the correct size, so that you use the minimum liquid

- Roasting – on a rack so that the food does not sit in fat; baste with fat-free liquids, such as wine or lemon juice

- Sautéing – use a high heat and a small amount of non-stick cooking spray, or just cook without spray if you have a good-quality non-stick pan

- Steaming – in a perforated basket over simmering water; add seasoning to the water for extra flavour

- Stir-frying – in a wok, using a small amount of non-stick cooking spray or a tiny amount of olive oil.

You can also increase flavour, reduce fat and salt content, and make the most of your ingredients' nutritional value if you

Remember to:

- Check labels for common ingredients, such as soy sauce, baking soda and monosodium glutamate – these all contain high levels of sodium and should be used very sparingly, if at all

- Make your own stock rather than using pre-prepared cubes, which can be high in salt

- Steam vegetables, for preference, in order to maximize both their flavour and nutritional value

- Cook lightly to preserve vitamin content (but cook meats and other foods that may harbour disease-producing organisms thoroughly)

- Choose extra virgin olive oil and vinegar rather than salted, pre-prepared salad dressings

Chopped, fresh herbs and garlic can be used to flavour your cooking, rather than using salt.

- Wash canned vegetables before use – by doing so you can substantially reduce their salt content

- Use only one egg yolk when making scrambled eggs or omelettes, but mix in two or three extra egg whites

- Trim as much fat as you can from meat before you cook it and remove the skin from poultry

- Choose lean, low-fat meats, such as game (but, again, remember to remove the skin) and venison

- Drain oil from canned fish and rinse the fish in water before you use it

- Use herbs, lemon juice, wine and freshly ground pepper to enhance flavours.

Sea food provides a superior source of nutrients, which are vital to growth and good health. These include high amounts of proteins, vitamins, minerals and unsaturated fats.

FISH STOCK

Ingredients

2 lb fish bones, heads (with gills removed) and tails (sole or plaice are tastiest, but any other white, non-oily fish will do)

1 large onion, coarsely chopped

2 shallots, coarsely chopped

2 ribs of celery, tops included, coarsely chopped

2 large carrots, scrubbed but not peeled, coarsely chopped

2 bay leaves

2 cloves

6 sprigs of parsley, coarsely chopped

1 tbsp peppercorns

Lemon rind from half a lemon

Cold water to cover

Method

Place everything in a stockpot and bring to simmering point – do not allow to boil. Simmer for 20–30 minutes, but no longer or the stock will become bitter. Strain through cheesecloth or use a non-metallic colander. Reduce the strained stock by boiling, if required. Use or freeze as required.

VEGETABLE STOCK

Ingredients

3 large carrots, scrubbed but not peeled, coarsely
    chopped

1 turnip, coarsely chopped

2 onions, coarsely chopped

2 leeks, coarsely chopped

4 ribs of celery, including tops, coarsely chopped

coarsely chopped trimmings from cauliflower, spinach,
    broccoli or any other vegetables, so long as they are
    fresh and clean. Always use fresh vegetables.

1 cup any dried beans, having been soaked overnight, if
    necessary; or use rice or barley

2 tbsp olive oil

1 bouquet garni, which includes 3 sprigs parsley,
    1 sprig thyme and 1 bay leaf

1 tbsp peppercorns

Approx 3.9 litres cold water for 1 kg vegetables

Method

Warm the olive oil in a stockpot, add the vegetables
and simmer, stirring continuously for 15 minutes until
they start to colour slightly. Then add the water and
the other ingredients and bring to simmering point.
Simmer for at least 2
hours, adding more
water if necessary. Then
strain through cheese-
cloth or use a non-
metallic colander. Use or
freeze, as required.

*Use the stocks for the basis
of soups and stews. Soups
are one of the easiest
things to make, and can be
made from nearly
anything. If you are
making a vegetable soup,
make sure the vegetables
of your choice are nice
and fresh as the flavour
will be so much better.*

CHICKEN STOCK

Ingredients

The bones of a chicken, and, if available, a ham bone
    or a veal knuckle (ask your butcher for one)

2 leeks, coarsely chopped

2 large carrots, scrubbed but not peeled, coarsely
    chopped

3 large onions, coarsely chopped

2 ribs of celery, tops included, coarsely chopped

6 sprigs of parsley, coarsely chopped

1 large clove garlic

2 cloves

1 tbsp peppercorns

Lemon rind from half a lemon

Method

Place the bones in a stockpot and cover with cold
water. Bring to simmering point – do not allow to boil.
Simmer for at least an hour, then add all other
ingredients and more cold water to cover, if necessary.
Return to simmering point and simmer for another 2
hours. Then strain through cheese-cloth or use a non-
metallic colander. Refrigerate, and when stock has set
remove any fat from the top. Use or freeze, as required.

Eating nutritiously is important, as well as getting plenty of exercise. If you need a snack, then the best things to eat are fresh fruit and vegetables that are high in vitamins and minerals.

A HEALTHY LIFESTYLE

Eating a healthy diet is only one part of the healthy heart lifestyle. To reduce blood pressure, lower cholesterol levels, promote cardiovascular health and improve the quality of your life, you should also:

● Give up smoking – if you smoke, you have more than double the risk of having a heart attack than a non-smoker, and you are more likely not to survive a heart attack

● Manage stress – use relaxation techniques and anger-management methods to cope with stress and keep your blood pressure low

● Lose weight – if you are overweight, you are between two and six times more likely to develop high blood pressure, but adopting the low GI diet will solve this problem.

● Cut down on alcohol – there's evidence to suggest that two units of alcohol, and especially of red wine, can reduce blood pressure, but more than this can increase blood pressure

● Lead an active life – even small amounts of physical activity, for example walking or gardening, can increase the number of calories that you burn and so help lose weight, as well as reducing the risk of developing heart disease.

TABLES

These tables give the nutritional values for the main ingredients used in the recipes that follow. To eat healthily and minimize your risk of developing insulin resistance, and also to minimize the risk of developing heart disease, the major part of your diet should consist of foods with a low or medium glycaemic index, a low fat content, moderate protein levels and a high fibre content. Use the Healthy Eating Pyramid on page 21 as a guide to the proportions of each type of food that you should eat.

Remember that carrying excess weight is a major risk for developing heart problems, and watch your calorie intake, too. Doctors recommend that men with a sedentary lifestyle – that of an office worker, say – should eat 2,700 calories a day, while women should eat 2,000. In order to lose weight gradually, at the rate of half a kg a week, you need to reduce this figure by 500 calories.

Food	Quantity	Glycaemic index	Fat	Protein	Fibre	Calories
Meat and Dairy						
Cheese, feta	20 g	M	6	4	0	80
Cheese, reduced fat	20 g	M	4.5	7	0	70
Chicken, skinless	100 g	L	5	30	0	150
Crème fraîche, low fat	100 g	M	17.5	3	0	800
Egg	1 medium	M	5.5	6	0	80
Lean beef, lamb, pork	100 g	M	7	30	0	190
Milk, low fat	250 ml	L	2.5	8	0	102
Rabbit	100 g	L	4.5	30	0	160
Wild fowl	100 g	L	6	30	0	155
Yoghurt	100 g	L	0	5	0	40
Fish						
Herring, salmon	100 g	L	11	20	0	180
Mackerel	100 g	L	18	25	0	220
Sardine	100 g	L	2	15	0	65
Shellfish	100 g	L	1	15	0	105
Trout	100 g	L	6	20	0	155
Tuna	100 g	L	3	20	0	120
White fish	100 g	L	2	20	0	90

Prawns are an excellent low-calorie choice, and they are a rich source of protein, vitamins and minerals.

Food	Quantity	Glycaemic index	Fat	Protein	Fibre	Calories
Fruit						
Apple	1 medium	L	0	0.5	2	45
Apricot	3	M	0	1.5	2	30
Banana	1 small	M	0.5	1	1	90
Berries, fresh	100 g	L	0	0.5	1	30
Dried fruit	50 g	M	0	0.5	4	80
Grapefruit	half	L	0	0.5	1	30
Melon	slice	M	0	0.5	1	50
Nectarine, peach	1 medium	L	0	0.5	1	35
Orange	1 medium	L	0	1.5	3	50

Fruit is easily digested and has many health benefits.

Vegetables						
Aubergine	100 g	L	0	0.5	2	75
Avocado	½ medium	L	15	2	3.5	150
Beans	100 g	L	0.5	6	4	100
Beetroot	small	L	0	0.5	0.5	25
Broccoli	100 g	L	0	1.5	2.5	25
Cabbage	50 g	L	0	1	1	7
Carrot	50 g	L	0	0.5	1	12

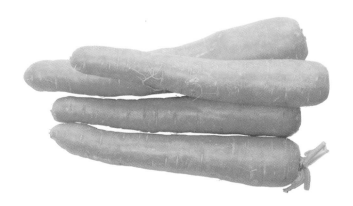

Carrots are high in beta-carotene (providing vitamin A value) and cooking carrots actually enhances the digestibility of the beta-carotene.

Food	Quantity	Glycaemic index	Fat	Protein	Fibre	Calories
Vegetables *(continued)*						
Cauliflower	100 g	L	0	1	1.5	20
Green beans	100 g	L	0	1.5	2.5	20
Onions	medium	L	0	1	1.4	30
Peas	100 g	L	0	3.5	6	60
Peppers	100 g	L	0	1	2.5	30
Potatoes, new	3	M	0	1.5	3	100
Soyabean	100 g	L	7	8	6	120
Spinach	50 g cooked	L	0	1	1	10
Squash, butternut	100 g	M	0	1	1.5	30
Sweetcorn	100 g	M	0.5	2.5	1.5	95
Tofu	100 g	L	4	8	0	70
Tomato	medium	L	0	1	1	15

Eating raw onions can help to increase your high-density lipoprotein cholesterol (HDL) levels. This good type of cholesterol can help to keep blood pressure low, so reducing the risk of cardiovascular disease and stroke.

Peppers are low in calories and are especially rich in vitamins A and C. Surprisingly, a pepper contains three to four times more vitamin C than an orange. They do not contain any fat.

Cereal, Nuts, Pulses

Food	Quantity	Glycaemic index	Fat	Protein	Fibre	Calories
Barley	50 g raw	L	1	2	1	140
Chickpeas	100 g	L	3	5	4	110
Lentils	100 g	L	0.5	8	2	100
Oats	50 g raw	L	1	4	3	140
Pasta, wholegrain	100 g	L	1	5	4	120
Rice, brown, basmati	100 g	M	0	3.5	1	200
Walnuts	2 tbsp	L	8	2	1	80
Wild rice	100 g	M	0	3	1	100

BREAKFASTS

APPLE AND DATE PORRIDGE

SERVES **4**

What better way to start the day than with a healthy, and filling, bowl of porridge. The apple and dates give the porridge an enjoyable sweetness, which can also be achieved with a variety of fruits.

100 g whole rolled porridge oats

15 g bran

473 ml semi-skimmed milk

300 ml water

2 eating apples, cored and chopped

75 g dried dates, stoned and chopped

2 tbsp dark brown muscovado sugar

1 Mix the porridge oats, bran, milk and water together in a saucepan.

2 Bring to the boil, stirring occasionally, then simmer for 6 minutes, stirring 3–4 times.

3 Stir in the apple and dates and simmer for a further 3–4 minutes, stirring occasionally.

4 Stir in half the sugar and spoon into 4 individual serving bowls. Sprinkle with the remaining sugar and serve.

NUTRITIONAL VALUES

RAISIN BRAN CRUNCH

SERVES **4**

The bran gives this dish a nice fruity crunch.

150 g raisins

525 g bran

200 g porridge oats

12 tbsp sesame seeds (unroasted)

10 tbsp sunflower seeds (unroasted)

240 ml less 2 tbsp unsweetened orange juice

NUTRITIONAL VALUES

1   Mix the raisins, bran, porridge oats and both types of seeds in a large bowl, then stir in the orange juice.

2   Preheat the oven to 160°C/gas mark 3.

3   Lightly grease a large roasting tin. Stir the mixture thoroughly, then turn it into the tin – do not press it down. Bake for about 2 hours, turning and stirring occasionally, until well browned, crisp and dry.

BANANA BRAN ENERGY

SERVES **4**

If you are unable to face a full breakfast in the morning, take your energy in a glass with this nutritious drink.

4 large bananas, peeled and cut into chunks

1 tbsp lemon juice

300 ml low-fat natural yoghurt

300 ml skimmed milk

2 tbsp honey

lemon slices and mint sprigs for garnish

1 Place all the ingredients in a food processor or blender. Liquidize for 1 minute until smooth. Pour into tall serving glasses, garnish and serve immediately.

NUTRITIONAL VALUES

APRICOT YOGHURT CRUNCH

SERVES **4**

A variation on a Scottish dish, the crunchy porridge oats, spicy yoghurt and lightly poached fruit make an attractive morning dish.

275 g apricots, pitted

3 tbsp honey

50 g porridge oats, toasted

$^{1}/_{2}$–1 tsp ground ginger

275 g low-fat natural yoghurt

1 Place the apricots in a pan with 150 ml water and 1 tbsp of the honey. Cook for 5 minutes until softened and drain.

2 Mix the oats and remaining honey in a bowl. Stir the ginger into the yoghurt.

3 Alternately layer the fruit, yoghurt and oat mixtures into serving glasses. Chill and serve.

NUTRITIONAL VALUES

WHOLEMEAL MORNING ROLLS

MAKES **18**

This is an overnight dough to make creamy, soft rolls in time for breakfast. There is nothing better than waking up to the smell of freshly baking bread – a marvellous way to impress your guests.

OVERNIGHT DOUGH

575 ml warm water

500 g wholemeal bread flour

1 tbsp salt substitute (see page 14)

1 packet active dry yeast

MORNING DOUGH

1 packet active dry yeast

175 ml warm water

575 g wholemeal bread flour

50 g margarine

1 tsp light muscovado suger

1 Place the water for the overnight dough in a large bowl. Add the flour, salt and yeast and mix lightly – do not beat or knead. Cover and leave overnight at room temperature.

2 In the morning, add all the remaining ingredients to the bowl and mix to a manageable dough; the margarine will be incorporated during the mixing. Turn out onto a floured surface and knead well for about 10 minutes until smooth and elastic.

3 Divide the dough into 18 pieces and shape them into rolls. Place them on lightly greased baking trays, quite close together so that they grow into each other and form a broken crust. Cover and leave in a warm place for 30 minutes to rise.

4 Preheat an oven to 220°C/gas mark 7. Bake the rolls for about 20 minutes. The bases will sound hollow when tapped, but the tops of the rolls will only brown slightly and remain soft. Cool on a wire rack.

NUTRITIONAL VALUES

HOMEMADE MUESLI

SERVES **4**

*Many whole-food shops sell bags of mixed grains ready for making muesli.
Otherwise, keep the mixture as plain or as varied as you like – a simple combination
of oatmeal (an excellent source of soluble fibre) and fruit is perfectly good.*

225 g porridge oats

150 g bran

75 g wheat or millet flakes

75 g raisins

75 g golden raisins

112 g chopped dried
 apple rings

150 g chopped ready-to-
 eat dried apricots

150 g chopped walnuts

1 Mix all the ingredients in a
large bowl, then store the
muesli in an airtight container
in a cool, dry place.

2 Serve with milk
(skimmed or low fat) or
natural yoghurt. Fresh
fruit, such as banana, grapes
or peach, may be served with
the muesli. For a special
breakfast, combine a selection
of chopped fresh fruits with the
muesli.

NUTRITIONAL VALUES

POTATO CAKES

SERVES **4**

If you prepare the spicy potato cake mixture in advance, it can be cooked quickly the next morning in a non-stick frying pan. The pancakes are especially good served with grilled tomatoes.

675 g potatoes, peeled or scraped

2 tbsp wholewheat flour, plus extra for dusting

2 tbsp bran cereal, crushed

1 small onion, grated

2 tbsp chopped parsley

1–2 tsp curry powder

salt substitute (see page 14)

3 tbsp semi-skimmed milk

oil, for brushing

parsley sprigs, to garnish

NUTRITIONAL VALUES

1 Soak the potatoes in cold water for about 30 minutes to remove some of the starch. Drain, rinse and dry them, and then grate coarsely into a bowl.

2 Stir in the flour, bran cereal, onion, parsley and curry powder to taste, and season with salt substitute. Lastly, stir in the milk and shape the mixture into a round. Divide it into 8 equal-sized pieces. Brush your hands with flour and shape the pieces into flat rounds. Sprinkle the potato cakes with wholemeal flour to cover them on all sides.

3 Lightly brush a non-stick frying pan with oil and heat it over a medium heat. Fry the potato cakes for 4–5 minutes on each side, until they are evenly brown. Serve them hot, garnished with parsley.

LIGHT MEALS

ROAST SQUASH, VEGETABLE AND PASTA SALAD

SERVES **4**

A filling salad that you can enjoy as a main course, or in smaller quantities as an appetizer.

4 x 2.5 cm slices crown prince squash, deseeded

2 yellow courgettes, trimmed

1 large aubergine, halved lengthways

1 large red pepper

1 garlic bulb

salt substitute (see page 14) and freshly ground
    black pepper

olive oil

200 g fresh or dried tagliatelli, spaghetti or other
    noodles

FOR DRESSING

6 tbsp extra virgin olive oil

2 tbsp balsamic vinegar

1 tsp Dijon mustard

fructose sugar or sweetener

Mixed salad leaves, to serve

1 Preheat a 220°C/gas mark 7 oven. Place all the vegetables in a roasting tin, season lightly and drizzle with olive oil. Roast for 40 minutes, or until they are tender and beginning to blacken. Turn the courgettes, pepper, and aubergine during cooking, and remove the vegetables as they are done.

2 Cover the peppers with a damp cloth as soon as they come out of the oven, then leave all the vegetables to cool. Peel the skins away from the peppers, then remove their cores and seeds.

3 Blend all the ingredients for the vinaigrette together and season well to taste. Cook the pasta, drain in a colander and shake briefly, then turn into a glass serving dish, and add half the vinaigrette. Toss, then leave to cool completely.

4 Peel the squash, then chop the roasted vegetables into bite-size pieces, and squeeze the garlic cloves from their skins. Pile the vegetables over the pasta, top with the salad leaves and pour over the remaining dressing. Toss just before serving.

NUTRITIONAL VALUES

SEAFOOD SALAD WITH BLACK BEAN PAPAYA SALSA

SERVES **4**

This is a delicious and unusual salad dish. Spicy and full of flavour, it is a real treat for the tastebuds.

mixed salad greens

350 g–450 g grilled salmon, chilled

BLACK BEAN-PAPAYA SALSA

450 g can of black beans, rinsed and drained

1 papaya, peeled, pitted and diced

2 roasted chilli peppers, peeled and chopped

75 g chopped red pepper

75 g chopped red onion

37 g chopped fresh coriander

1 tsp finely minced fresh ginger

37 g fresh lime juice

1 tsp crushed dried red
   chilli

salt substitute (see page
   14) and pepper to taste

1   To make the salsa, mix all the ingredients together. Let stand for 30 minutes, then taste and adjust the seasoning.

2   Clean and tear the salad greens and divide them among 4 plates.

3   Break the salmon into chunks, removing any bones. Divide the salmon among the plates. Top each salad with 8 tablespoons black bean papaya salsa. Serve at once.

WARM PASTA SALAD

SERVES **4**

This salad combines the saltiness of green olives, the crunch of walnuts and the goodness of fresh vegetables. The flavours are enhanced when this salad is served warm, but if you have cold leftovers add a splash of vinaigrette for flavour.

225 g pasta shapes

125 g asparagus

4 tbsp extra virgin olive oil

4 tbsp freshly grated Parmesan cheese plus extra for sprinkling

1 courgette, finely grated

4 spring onions, sliced

25 g walnuts, chopped

8 green olives, stoned

salt substitute (see page 14) and freshly ground black pepper

1 Cook pasta according to directions on package. While the pasta is cooking, blanch the asparagus for 2–3 minutes in boiling water. Drain asparagus, and cut into 2.5 cm pieces.

2 When the pasta is cooked, drain but do not rinse, then put it in a large mixing bowl. Pour olive oil over pasta, and toss with two forks. Add the Parmesan, and toss again. Stir in the asparagus, courgette, spring onions, walnuts and green olives. Add salt and pepper to taste. Serve with a sprinkling of Parmesan over the top.

NUTRITIONAL VALUES

PASTA NIÇOISE WITH BALSAMIC DRESSING

SERVES **4 – 6**

The pungent sweetness of balsamic vinegar adds a new dimension to this traditional salad.

SALAD

175 g French beans, trimmed

200 g can tuna, drained

275 g cooked fresh pasta, such as fusilli

2 tbsp chopped fresh flat leaf parsley

2 large tomatoes, sliced

2 medium hard-boiled eggs, shelled and sliced

50 g can anchovy fillets, drained (soaked if
   preferred)

8 stoned black olives

DRESSING

5 tbsp extra virgin olive oil

1 tsp clear honey

1 tsp wholegrain mustard

salt substitute (see page 14) and freshly ground
   black pepper

2 tbsp balsamic vinegar

1 Cook the French beans in a pan of lightly salted boiling water for 4–5 minutes or until just cooked. Drain and plunge into cold water. Drain again and reserve. Divide the drained tuna into small chunks.

2 Mix the pasta and chopped parsley together and place in the base of a shallow serving platter or dish. Arrange the cooked beans, sliced tomatoes, tuna, eggs, drained anchovies and olives attractively on top of the pasta.

3 Place the dressing ingredients in a screw-top jar and shake vigorously. Pour over the salad just before serving.

NUTRITIONAL VALUES

MALASA RICE WITH POTATOES

A light meal that has a punch of flavour.

225 g potatoes

225 g long-grain rice

2 tbsp olive oil

75 g onion, chopped

2–3 cloves

1.2 cm piece cinnamon stick

1 black cardamom pod, bruised or slit

2–3 bay leaves

½ tsp cumin seeds

2 tsp ginger and garlic paste

¼ tsp turmeric

½ tsp chilli powder

¾ tsp salt substitute (see page 14)

1 tbsp low-fat natural yoghurt

1 green chilli, chopped

1 Scrub the potatoes well, do not peel them, then cut them into eighths.

2 Wash and soak the rice for 10–15 minutes, then drain it well and keep it to one side.

3 Heat the oil in a medium-sized heavy saucepan, add the onion, the cloves, cinnamon stick, cardamom pod and cumin seeds and fry until the onion turns a rich golden colour.

4 Add the ginger and garlic paste, turmeric, chilli powder and salt substitute (see page 14). Stir and cook the spices well, then add the yoghurt and 1 tablespoon of water to prevent it sticking and burning.

5 Add 425 ml of water, let it come to the boil, then add the rice, potatoes and green chilli. Cover the pan tightly and simmer for about 25 minutes. Then let it stand for another 3-4 minutes before serving.

NUTRITIONAL VALUES

MINTED PEPPER SALAD

SERVES **4**

Make this cool, light and colourful salad for a summer lunch or picnic, but do not drizzle over the olive oil until ready to serve.

400 g dried macaroni

dash of olive oil, plus extra for
    drizzling

1 yellow pepper, cored,
    deseeded and cut into
    diamonds

1 green pepper, cored, seeded
    and cut into diamonds

400 g artichoke hearts, drained
    and quartered

15 cm piece of cucumber, sliced

handful of mint leaves

freshly ground black pepper

125 g freshly grated Parmesan
    cheese

1   Bring a saucepan of water to the boil, and add the macaroni with a dash of olive oil. Cook for 10 minutes, until tender. Drain, rinse then place in a mixing bowl.

2   Mix the remaining ingredients into the pasta. Drizzle some olive oil over the salad, then serve.

NUTRITIONAL VALUES

COUSCOUS WITH DRIED APRICOTS AND ALMONDS

SERVES **8**

A very tasty dish with its fruit and nut combination.

350 g precooked couscous

125 g ready-to-eat dried apricots, sliced into strips

salt substitute (see page 14) and freshly ground
   black pepper

225 g blanched almonds, lightly toasted

chopped fresh coriander, to serve

olive oil, to serve (optional)

1 Put the couscous in a bowl and pour over 570 ml water. Leave for about 30 minutes or until most of the water has been absorbed; stir frequently with a fork to keep the grains separate.

2 Stir the apricots and seasoning into the couscous then tip into a steamer or metal colander lined with cheese-cloth. Place over a saucepan of boiling water, cover tightly with aluminium foil, and steam for about 20 minutes until hot. Stir in the almonds, coriander and olive oil, if using.

NUTRITIONAL VALUES

GADO-GADO

This is a traditional dish in Indonesia, where it is served widely. It is also a favourtite in Indonesian restaurants around the world.

175 g firm white cabbage, grated

1 small onion, minced

2 cloves garlic, crushed

1 tbsp oil, preferably peanut

pinch of chilli powder

1.2 cm fresh ginger, peeled and grated

2 tbsp peanut butter

hot water

175 g bean sprouts

175 g cucumber, peeled and cubed

75 g salted peanuts (optional)

1 fresh green chilli pepper, deseeded and thinly
    sliced (optional)

1   Blanch the cabbage in lots of boiling water for 3 minutes, drain and leave to cool.

2   Fry the onion and garlic in the oil until lightly browned, then add the spices and fry for a minute more.

3   Turn down the heat and add the peanut butter and enough hot water to make the sauce a creamy consistency.

4   Combine the cooled cabbage, bean sprouts and cucumber, pour the hot sauce over them and serve at once, garnished, if you like, with peanuts and fresh chilli pepper.

NUTRITIONAL VALUES

HARICOT BEAN AND COTTAGE CHEESE

SERVES **4 – 8**

This makes a very colourful dish, as well as tasting delicious.

225 g haricot beans

¼ tsp bicarbonate of soda

150 ml French dressing

4 spring onions, washed and sliced

1 green pepper, deseeded

1 red pepper, deseeded

½ grated Iceberg lettuce

8 tsp cottage cheese

20 stuffed olives, to garnish

1 Soak the haricot beans in cold water for at least 8 hours. Drain and pour into a saucepan, cover with cold water, add the bicarbonate of soda and bring to the boil. Simmer for 30 minutes until cooked. Drain and allow to cool in a bowl.

2 Add the dressing to the cooked beans, then stir in the spring onions.

3 Cut the peppers into thin strips and mix with the beans.

4 Arrange the shredded lettuce on a round dish, leaving a decorative ring around the edge. Inside the lettuce ring, arrange a ring of cottage cheese.

5 Tip the dressed bean salad into the centre of the cottage cheese ring. Garnish with whole stuffed olives. Serve with sliced wholemeal bread.

NUTRITIONAL VALUES

MIXED BEAN AND TOFU SALAD

SERVES **6**

An excellent salad to serve as part of a buffet spread, as its tangy dressing provides a good contrast to creamier dressings such as sour cream or mayonnaise. It can also be served as an accompaniment to a meat or fish main course, or on its own.

FOR THE DRESSING

juice of 2 limes

6 tbsp olive oil

2 tbsp chopped fresh coriander

salt substitute (see page 14) and pepper

FOR THE SALAD

250 g firm tofu, cubed

175 g green beans, halved

425 g canned red kidney beans, drained and
    rinsed

425 g canned flageolet beans, drained and rinsed

1 avocado, peeled and sliced

mixed salad leaves

1 For the dressing, shake the ingredients together in a screw-top jar or whisk until combined. Pour the dressing over the tofu in a bowl, cover and chill until required.

2 For the salad, cook the green beans in a pan of boiling water for 5 minutes. Drain and cool under cold water. Pat dry with kitchen towels and add to the tofu with the kidney beans and flageolet beans. Add the avocado just before serving.

3 Spoon the salad on to a bed of lettuce leaves and serve.

NUTRITIONAL VALUES

CHILLI-SPICED BROCCOLI

SERVES **4**

This dish is from southern Italy. Use a chilli that is not too hot, with just enough bite to make it 'all arrabbiata' (angry), the term given in Italy to chilli-spiced dishes. The spicy broccoli can be mixed into spaghetti.

1 large or 2 medium-sized bunches broccoli,
    broken into florets, the stems peeled and cut into
    bite-sized pieces
salt substitute (see page 14) to taste
2 tbsp extra virgin olive oil
3–5 cloves garlic, sliced thin
1 medium hot or mild fresh red chilli, or more as
    desired, sliced thin or chopped
juice of ¼ to ½ lemon or to taste
grated Parmesan cheese (optional)

1 Blanch the broccoli in boiling water to which a
pinch of salt substitute has been added. Cook for
only a minute or two, or until the broccoli is
crisp-tender and bright green. Remove from the
heat, rinse well in cold water, and dry.

2 In a wok or large frying pan heat the olive oil,
garlic and chilli, and warm through, then add the
broccoli and cook together, seasoning with a little
salt, for a few minutes to meld the flavours.
Squeeze the lemon juice over the vegetables and
remove from the heat.

3 Serve the broccoli and red chillies hot, with a
grating of Parmesan cheese if wished, or at room
temperature, with a little more lemon juice
drizzled over the top.

NUTRITIONAL VALUES

MACARONI AND CHEESE WITH CHILLIES AND CHÈVRE

SERVES **4**

Macaroni and cheese is a classic comfort food, especially when the weather is cold. This version includes goat's cheese and mild chillies.

350 g macaroni

4 tbsp butter

1 tbsp plain flour

240 g semi-skimmed milk

salt substitute (see page 14) and a few pinches
    cayenne pepper to taste

grated nutmeg to taste

1–2 mild green chillies, roasted, peeled and sliced

75–125 g chèvre or other mild goat's cheese

several generous pinches thyme

2–3 cloves garlic, chopped

1 tbsp paprika

275 g grated mild white cheese, such as
    mozzarella, cheddar or fontina, or a combination

1 Preheat the oven to 190°C/gas mark 5. Cook the pasta until tender but firm to the bite, then drain.

2 Heat the butter until foamy then sprinkle in the flour and cook for a few minutes. Remove from the heat and whisk in the milk. Cook, whisking, until the sauce thickens.

3 Combine the pasta with the sauce, season with salt substitute, cayenne pepper and nutmeg, then add the sliced chili and the goat's cheese, a few tablespoons of sour cream to taste, if using, thyme, garlic, paprika and two-thirds of the cheese.

4 Arrange in a baking tin and top with the remaining cheese. Bake until lightly browned, and the macaroni hot and sizzling, about 20 minutes. You could garnish with some roasted chillies and a dusting of paprika if liked. Serve immediately.

NUTRITIONAL VALUES

RUSSIAN SALAD

The eggs and tuna in this recipe blend well together to give a great flavour to this light meal.

8 medium potatoes

1 medium carrot, cut into cubes

150 g fresh peas

2 hard-boiled eggs, cooled, peeled, and cut into
   cubes

200 g can water-packed tuna, drained, and flaked

1 red pepper, cut into cubes

75 g corn

75 g black olives

225 g low-fat mayonnaise

1 Put the potatoes in a large saucepan of water and bring to the boil. Cover, lower the heat, and simmer for about 20–25 minutes, or until the potatoes are done. Drain, and when cool, cut into $\frac{1}{4}$ in cubes.

2 Boil the carrot and peas for 3–5 minutes, until lightly cooked. Drain.

3 Mix the potato with the egg, tuna, carrot, peas, pepper, corn and olives in a large salad bowl.

4 Just before serving, add the mayonnaise to the salad, and toss to coat.

NUTRITIONAL VALUES

TORTELLINI COLESLAW

SERVES **4 – 6**

Ideal as a snack or a starter for a meal on a hot summer's day.

225 g stuffed tortellini, cooked

3 tbsp olive oil

1 tbsp white wine vinegar

1 tsp French mustard

salt substitute (see page 14) and freshly ground
    black pepper

black olives, to garnish

COLESLAW

½ cabbage

1 carrot, scraped and grated

2 tbsp raisins

2 sticks celery, washed

75 g low-fat mayonnaise

1 Place the cooked tortellini (after rinsing in cold water and drained) in a bowl.

2 Mix the dressing by placing the oil, vinegar, mustard and seasoning in a screw-top jar. Shake well and pour over the pasta.

3 Make the coleslaw by washing, draining and shredding the cabbage. Mix in a separate bowl with the grated carrot and raisins.

4 After washing the celery remove the strings with a sharp knife and then chop into thin slices, add to the cabbage and season well.

5 Mix the low-fat mayonnaise into the vegetable mixture.

6 Arrange rows of coleslaw with alternating rows of tortellini for a pretty and delicious salad.

NUTRITIONAL VALUES

STIR-FRIED EGG NOODLES WITH TOFU, RED PEPPER AND MANGETOUT

SERVES **4**

With its combination of noodles and tofu, this is an archetypal Asian dish. Like much of the cooking from the region, it is quick and easy to prepare.

275 g dried medium egg noodles

1 tbsp sesame oil

125 g mangetout, halved

1 tbsp olive oil

1 clove garlic, finely chopped

6 spring onions, sliced

1 red pepper, deseeded and sliced

6 tinned water chestnuts, sliced

125 g pak choy, chopped

275 g firm tofu, diced into 1.2 cm cubes

1 tbsp oyster sauce

3 tbsp Chinese light soy sauce

1 tsp sugar

1 Cook the egg noodles in a pan of boiling water for 4 minutes. Drain and sprinkle 1 tablespoon of sesame oil over them. Blanch the mangetouts in another pan of boiling water for 2 minutes, and drain.

2 Heat the sunflower oil in a wok or frying pan, and stir-fry the garlic and ginger for 1 minute.

3 Add the spring onions, red pepper, water chestnuts and pak choy, and stir fry for 2–3 minutes.

4 Add the tofu and stir-fry for 2 minutes. Add the oyster sauce, soy sauce and sugar and stir-fry for another 1–2 minutes. Serve hot.

NUTRITIONAL VALUES

SCALLOPS WITH COURGETTES AND TOMATO PASTA

SERVES **4 – 6**

Grilled scallops are sweet, tasty and easy to cook. Here is a great meal that can be made in about 30 minutes or less.

450 g linguini pasta

50 ml olive oil

4 garlic cloves, crushed

2 medium courgettes, diced

1 tsp salt substitute (see page 14)

1 tsp freshly ground black pepper

½ tsp crushed red pepper

50 g chopped basil leaves

4 plum tomatoes, diced

700 g sea scallops

olive oil

2 tbsp freshly grated Parmesan

1   Cook the pasta in a large pan of boiling water until tender but still firm to the bite.

2   In a frying pan on the hob or on your grill, heat the oil and sauté over a medium heat for 8–10 minutes or until tender and crisp. Add the basil and tomato and simmer for 5–7 minutes. Remove from the heat and keep warm.

3   Brush the scallops with olive oil and grill over medium-hot heat, 3 minutes per side, until the scallops are opaque. Remove the scallops, quarter them and add to the sauce mixture.

4   Transfer the pasta to a large serving platter or bowl. Pour the sauce over the cooked pasta and sprinkle with the Parmesan.

NUTRITIONAL VALUES

CHILLI-RICE BURGERS

These burgers can be grilled on the barbecue, but it is a good idea to put them in a grill basket so they can be easily turned over.

3 tbsp olive oil

2 cloves garlic, crushed

4 red chillies, deseeded and chopped

40 g long-grain rice, uncooked

1 large carrot, grated

2 tbsp tomato purée mixed with 2 tbsp water

570 ml vegetable stock, plus 1 to 2 tbsp

salt substitute (see page 14) and freshly ground
    black pepper, to taste

225 g canned kidney beans, drained

90 g corn kenels

2 tbsp chopped coriander

1 large tomato, sliced

6 buns, lightly toasted

chilli pepper relish, to serve

NUTRITIONAL VALUES

1 Heat 2 tablespoons oil in a frying pan and sauté the garlic and chilli for 5 minutes. Stir in the rice and continue to cook for 3 minutes, stirring occasionally. Stir in the carrot.

2 Add the tomato purée mixture, vegetable stock, salt substitute and pepper to the frying pan. Bring to the boil. Reduce the heat and simmer for 20 minutes, or until the rice is cooked, stirring occasionally and adding a little extra stock if necessary.

3 Add the kidney beans and corn. Cook for another 5 minutes or until the mixture is very stiff and will stick together. Stir in the coriander and remove from the heat. Leave to cool.

4 When the mixture is cool enough to handle, wet your hands slightly and shape the mixture into 6 large burgers. Cover and refrigerate for at least 30 minutes.

5 Brush the burgers with olive oil and grill over medium heat for 4–5 minutes, turn carefully and cook for another 3–4 minutes or until heated through. To serve, place the burgers on the buns and top with a little chilli pepper relish.

SPIRALS WITH GRAPES AND GOATS CHEESE

SERVES **4**

This is delicious for a light lunch or as a starter. Serve with slices of French bread.

2 slices round chèvre goat's cheese, each cut in
    8 small wedges

175 g seedless green grapes

2 bunches of watercress, trimmed and roughly
    shredded

4 spring onions, chopped

grated rind and juice of 1
    orange

4 tbsp olive oil

freshly ground black
    pepper

350 g pasta spirals

1   Mix the cheese, grapes, watercress and spring onions in a large bowl.

2   Pour in the orange rind and juice and olive oil, then add plenty of freshly ground black pepper. Mix well.

3   Divide the hot, freshly drained pasta among 4 serving plates, then top each with a quarter of the cheese mixture. Serve at once.

NUTRITIONAL VALUES

GOOD TOMATO SAUCE

SERVES **4 – 6**

Good fresh pasta and a rich tomato sauce, topped with some freshly grated Parmesan cheese, is a simple yet splendid meal, particularly if there is a really fresh, crisp green salad as an accompaniment.

2 tbsp olive oil

1 large onion, chopped

1 carrot, chopped

1 celery stick, chopped

1 garlic clove, crushed

1 bay leaf

2 thyme sprigs

4 parsley sprigs

1 tbsp plain flour

2 tbsp tomato purée

875 g ripe tomatoes, roughly chopped

1 tbsp sugar substitute

5 fl oz dry red wine

salt substitute (see page 14) and freshly ground black
    pepper freshly grated Parmesan cheese, to serve

1 Heat the oil in a large, heavy-based saucepan. Add the onion, carrot, celery, garlic, bay leaf, thyme and parsley. Cook, stirring, for about 10 minutes, until the onion is softened slightly but not browned.

2 Stir in the flour and tomato purée. Then add the tomatoes and sugar substitute and stir in the wine. Add some seasoning, bring to the boil and give the sauce a good stir. Reduce the heat, cover the pan and leave to simmer for 1 hour.

3 Remove the bay leaf and herb sprigs, then purée the sauce in a liquidizer and rub it through a sieve to remove the seeds. Reheat and taste for seasoning before serving. Ladle the sauce over the pasta and top with Parmesan cheese to taste.

NUTRITIONAL VALUES

STUFFED COURGETTES

SERVES **4 – 6**

A delicious combination of tender courgette and fresh coriander mixed with a sweet soya sauce. You can make the filling and the sauce a day in advance. Reheat the sauce while the courgettes are baking.

125 g dried vermicelli, broken into small pieces

dash of olive oil

4 medium-sized courgettes

finely chopped walnuts, to garnish

FOR THE FILLING

150 ml sweet soy sauce

1 clove garlic, crushed

50 g mushrooms, very finely chopped

salt substitute (see page 14) and freshly ground
  black pepper

FOR THE SAUCE

4 tbsp olive oil

2 cloves garlic, crushed

25 g chopped fresh coriander

salt substitute(see page 14 and freshly ground
  black pepper

3 tbsp vegetable stock

1 Bring a large saucepan of water to the boil and add the vermicelli with a dash of olive oil. Cook for about 5 minutes, stirring occasionally, until tender. Drain and set aside.

2 Cut a thin slice lengthways along the top of each courgette and chop this piece finely. Using a teaspoon, scoop out the flesh from the middle of the courgette and chop roughly. Arrange the hollowed courgettes in a shallow ovenproof dish and set aside. Preheat the oven to 200°C/ gas mark 6.

3 To make the filling, place the sweet soy sauce and the garlic in a large frying pan and heat gently. Cook for about 1 minute, then stir in the mushrooms. Cook for about 5 minutes, then stir in the chopped walnuts and season to taste with salt substitute and freshly ground black pepper. Simmer for about 1–2 minutes, then stir in the vermicelli.

4 Remove from the heat and, using a teaspoon, stuff the courgettes with the filling, placing any extra around the courgettes in the dish. Cover the dish with aluminium foil and bake for 25–30 minutes, until the courgettes are tender.

5 Meanwhile, to make the sauce, place all the ingredients in a food processor or blender and purée until smooth. Transfer to a small saucepan and heat gently until warm. Remove the stuffed courgettes from the oven and serve with the coriander sauce, garnished with finely chopped walnuts.

NUTRITIONAL VALUES

EASTERN PASTA SALAD

A traditional combination of mint and lemon makes this dish a salad for summer. Choose your favourite pasta shapes for this recipe and serve with warm pitta bread to mop up the delicious dressing.

350 g dried pasta

dash of olive oil

400 g can chickpeas, drained

4 tbsp chopped fresh mint

finely grated zest of 1 lemon

FOR THE DRESSING

3 cloves garlic, crushed

6 tbsp extra virgin olive oil

3 tbsp white wine vinegar

freshly squeezed juice of 1 lemon

freshly ground black pepper

1 Bring a large saucepan of water to the boil and add the pasta with a dash of olive oil. Cook for about 10 minutes, stirring occasionally, until tender. Drain and rinse under cold water. Drain again and place in a large mixing bowl.

2 Add the chickpeas, mint and lemon zest to the pasta. Place all the dressing ingredients in a screw-top jar and shake well to mix. Pour the dressing over the chickpea mixture and mix well to combine. Cover and chill for at least 30 minutes. Toss before serving.

NUTRITIONAL VALUES

FATTOUSH

SERVES **4**

This salad of stale bread and salad vegetables from Lebanon, characteristically dressed with lots of olive oil and lemon, is very refreshing. A sprinkle of sumac – a tart, red berry related to poison sumac, but not harmful – gives a distinctive tang. Great to serve with a helping of low-fat yoghurt.

1 large or 2 small cucumbers, diced

3 ripe tomatoes, diced

1 green pepper, diced

25 g (about 8 tbsp) each: fresh mint, fresh
   chopped coriander, fresh chopped parsley

3 spring onions, thinly sliced

1 tsp salt substitute (see page 14)

3 garlic cloves. chopped

75 ml extra virgin olive oil

juice of 3 lemons

1 tsp sumac

3–4 pitta breads, stale and lightly toasted, then
   broken into pieces

1 Combine the cucumbers, tomatoes, pepper, mint, coriander, parsley, spring onions, salt substitute, garlic, olive oil, lemon juice and sumac. Chill for at least 1 hour. Just before serving, toss with the broken pitta breads.

NUTRITIONAL VALUES

TROUT AND PRAWN RISOTTO

SERVES **4**

Smoked trout has been used in this flavourful and colourful dish. If unavailable, unsmoked trout fillets would also be delicious.

1 litre fish stock

150 ml dry white wine

50 g butter

1 leek, sliced

1 garlic clove, crushed

250 g arborio rice

1 green pepper, seeded and chopped

2 tsp fennel seeds

350 g smoked trout fillets, cut into chunks

125 g shelled cooked prawns

1 tbsp chopped fresh parsley

2 tbsp freshly grated Parmesan cheese

lime wedges, to serve

1 Pour the stock and wine into a saucepan and bring to the boil. Reduce the heat to a gentle simmer.

2 Meanwhile, melt the butter in a large frying pan and gently cook the leek and garlic for 2 minutes, stirring. Add the rices and cook gently, stirring, for 2 minutes until the rice is well coated in butter.

3 Add a ladleful of stock and wine mixture to the rice and cook gently, stirring, until absorbed. Continue adding small quantities of stock until half of the stock mixture has been used. Add the green pepper and fennel.

4 Continue adding the stock for a further 20 minutes. Add the fish and prawn and cook for a further 5 minutes, stirring gently, adding any remaining stock until the risotto is thick but not sticky.

5 Just before serving , add the parsley and cheese; serve in a warm bowl with lime wedges.

NUTRITIONAL VALUES

STARTERS

KRUPNICK

Polish mushroom and barley soup with celeriac. A big bowl of steaming mushroom barley soup is great when it's really cold.

1 carrot, sliced

1 onion, chopped

1 leek, chopped

2 tbsp olive oil

250–350 g barley

15 g mixed dried mushrooms

1.5–1.8 litre stock

3 garlic cloves, cut into chunks (optional)

$^1/_4$–$^1/_2$ celeriac, peeled and diced

2–3 bay leaves

1 large potato, diced

salt substitute (see page 14) and freshly ground
   black pepper, to taste

chopped fresh parsley, to serve

NUTRITIONAL VALUES

1 Lightly sauté the carrot, onion and leek in the olive oil until softened, about 5–10 minutes. Add the barley, mushrooms, stock, garlic, if using, celeriac and bay leaves. Bring to the boil, reduce the heat and simmer until the barley is half tender, about 20 minutes.

2 Add the potato and continue to cook until the potato and barley are very tender. If the soup is too thick, add more stock; if it is too thin, boil it down to reduce a little.

3 Test for seasoning and serve with parsley scattered over.

GARLICKY PASTA AND BEAN SOUP

SERVES **4**

This recipe is based on the traditional Italian soup called 'pasta e fagioli', which you will find on many restaurant menus. The soup's flavour will be greatly enhanced if a good-quality chicken stock is used for the broth.

1 tbsp olive oil

1 onion, finely chopped

4 garlic cloves, crushed

400 g can canellini beans, drained and rinsed

1.7 litre chicken or vegetable stock

100 g small pasta shapes or spaghetti broken into
    small pieces

salt substitute (see page 14) and freshly ground
    black pepper

crusty bread, to serve

1 Heat the oil in a large frying pan over a medium heat. Add the chopped onion and sauté it gently for about 3 minutes without allowing it to brown. Add the crushed garlic and continue to sauté for a further 2 minutes. Add the canellini beans, stock, pasta and seasoning and bring to the boil. Reduce the heat and simmer for 10–15 minutes.

2 Transfer to a warmed soup tureen and serve with plenty of crusty bread.

NUTRITIONAL VALUES

IRISH BARLEY SOUP

SERVES **6**

Leeks grew wild in Ireland for many centuries and they are still as much part of the Irish diet as oats and barley. Combining pearl barley with leeks in this tasty soup makes a very traditional dish.

290 g leeks, finely sliced

2 tbsp olive oil

50 g shredded spinach

50 g pearl barley

1.8 litre well-flavoured chicken or vegetable stock

bouquet garni

salt substitute (see page 14) and freshly ground
    black pepper

2 bay leaves

50 ml low-fat crème fraîche (optional)

1 Cook the leeks in the oil until softened but not browned, then add the spinach and cook briefly until wilted. Add the barley, stock and bouquet garni, then bring to the boil. Season lightly and add the bay leaves, then cover the pan and simmer for about 1^1/$_2$ hours until the barley is tender.

2 Remove the bouquet garni and bay leaves. Season to taste, then stir in the low-fat crème fraîche, if using, and serve immediately with fresh crusty bread.

NUTRITIONAL VALUES

MINESTRONE SOUP

SERVES **4 – 6**

There are many versions of this classic soup; this one is simple, wholesome and filling. Serve with warm, crusty garlic bread.

1 tbsp extra virgin olive oil

3 garlic cloves, crushed

450 g carrots, peeled and finely diced

450 g courgettes, finely diced

75 g dried pastina (any tiny pasta shapes)

5 tbsp chopped fresh parsley

50 g vegetable paste

1.7 litres well-flavoured vegetable stock

salt substitute (see page 14) and freshly ground
    black pepper

freshly grated Parmesan cheese, to serve

1 Heat the olive oil in a large pan and add the garlic. Sauté for about 2 minutes, then stir in the diced carrots and courgettes. Cook for about 5 minutes, stirring occasionally.

2 Stir the pastina and chopped parsley into the vegetable mixture, add the vegetable paste and vegetable stock, and season with salt and ground black pepper.

3 Cover and simmer for about 30 minutes, until the vegetables and pasta have softened and the flavours have developed. Serve with freshly grated Parmesan cheese.

NUTRITIONAL VALUES

FAMILY LENTIL SOUP

SERVES **4**

This makes a delicious meal for those cold nights in. Why not try it with different vegetables to make a delicious meal all of your own.

2 tbsp olive oil

1 large onion, peeled

1 carrot, scraped

2 sticks celery, washed

225 g red lentils, washed

1 sprig parsley

1 bay leaf

1 bouquet garni

salt substitute (see page 14) and freshly ground
   black pepper

1.2 litres stock

1 tbsp chopped parsley

wholemeal bread croûtons

1 Heat the olive oil over a low heat in a large saucepan.

2 Dice the vegetables finely, add to the olive oil and allow to cook for 4 minutes.

3 Add the washed lentils, parsley, bay leaf, bouquet garni, seasoning and stock. Bring to the boil and simmer gently for about 35 minutes, until the lentils are cooked. If necessary, skim the surface from time to time.

4 Taste for seasoning and adjust. Serve with chopped parsley sprinkled on top and a dish of croûtons.

NUTRITIONAL VALUES

PUMPKIN SOUP

SERVES **4**

Pumpkin doesn't just have to be used for Halloween, but can be enjoyed all year round in this delicious soup.

1 tbsp olive oil

1 onion, chopped

350 g pumpkin or squash, peeled, pips removed
   and diced

225 g carrots, diced

2 potatoes, diced

600 ml vegetable stock

2 small courgettes, thinly sliced

freshly ground black pepper

chopped parsley, to garnish

1 Place the oil and onion in a saucepan and cook for 2–3 minutes, to soften.

2 Add the pumpkin or squash, carrots, potatoes and stock. Bring to the boil, cover and simmer for 15 minutes, or until the vegetables are nearly tender.

3 Add the courgettes and cook for 5 minutes more.

4 Purée half the soup, blend with the remaining soup and season with pepper, to taste.

5 Reheat if necessary and serve in individual bowls. Make sure some of the courgettes float on the top to decorate.

6 Sprinkle with parsley to serve.

NUTRITIONAL VALUES

LENTIL AND TOMATO SOUP

SERVES **4**

Tomato soup is real comfort food, perfect for a cold winter's day or for when you need a taste of childhood. The lentils help to give the soup more texture.

200 g red lentils

1 onion, chopped

2 carrots, grated

600 ml vegetable stock

2 bay leaves

400 g can tomatoes

2 tbsp tomato purée

1 tsp oregano, chopped

freshly ground black pepper

2 tbsp low-fat natural yoghurt

1 Wash the lentils, remove and discard any that are discoloured. Place in a large saucepan with the onion, carrot, stock and bay leaves.

2 Bring to the boil, cover and simmer for 25 minutes. Add the tomatoes with their juice, tomato purée and oregano. Bring back to the boil and simmer for 15 minutes or until lentils are soft. Season with black pepper.

3 Place in a liquidizer or food processor and lightly purée. Reheat and serve in individual bowls topped with a swirl of yoghurt.

NUTRITIONAL VALUES

WATERCRESS, ORANGE AND TOFU SOUP

SERVES **4**

A hearty vegetable soup thickened with puréed tofu. If firm tofu is more readily available it can be used instead of soft, but extra stock or water may be needed to achieve the right consistency.

600 ml chicken or vegetable stock

200 g potatoes, peeled and cut into small chunks

1 bunch of watercress, coarse stalks removed

250 g soft tofu

150 ml fresh orange juice

2 tbsp olive oil

2 leeks, thinly sliced

1 courgette, shredded

salt substitute (see page 14) and freshly ground
    black pepper

blanched grated leek and snipped chives, to
    garnish

crusty bread, to serve

1 In a large saucepan, bring the stock to a boil. Add the potatoes, cover the pan and simmer for 10 minutes or until tender. Chop the watercress and add to the pan. Simmer for 5 minutes.

2 Pour the soup into a food processor, add the orange juice and tofu and purée until smooth.

3 Rinse out the frying pan and place over a low heat. Add the olive oil and sauté the leeks and courgette until soft. Pour in the puréed soup and season to taste.

4 Reheat gently without boiling, garnish with blanched grated leek and snipped chives, and serve with crusty bread.

NUTRITIONAL VALUES

PASTA BEAN SOUP

SERVES **4 – 6**

A nutritious meal in itself – low-fat and full of protein.

2 tbsp olive oil

3 garlic cloves, crushed

4 tbsp chopped fresh parsley

150 g dried wholemeat gnocchi piccoli (shells)

1.5 litre vegetable broth

3 tbsp vegetable or tomato paste

400 g can mixed beans, such as borlotti, kidney, cannellini etc, drained

salt substitute and freshly ground black pepper

freshly grated Parmesan cheese, to serve

NUTRITIONAL VALUES

1 Heat the olive oil in a large saucepan and sauté the garlic with the chopped parsley for about 2 minutes. Add the gnocchi piccoli and cook for 1–2 minutes, stirring constantly.

2 Pour in the vegetable broth and add the vegetable or tomato paste. Bring to the boil, reduce the heat, then simmer for about 10 minutes, stirring occasionally, until the paste is tender.

3 Add the beans and season with the salt and freshly ground black pepper. Continue to cook for a further 5 minutes, then serve with a little freshly grated Parmesan cheese.

VEGETABLE BROTH

This traditional broth can be served as a starter or even as a meal in itself. The ideal accompaniment is crusty, wholegrain bread.

2 tbsp olive oil

2 onions, peeled and finely chopped

2 carrots, scraped and diced

1 small turnip, peeled and diced

2 sticks of celery, washed

1 litre water or stock

2 tbsp tomato purée

1 bouquet garni

1 bay leaf

1/2 tsp mixed herbs

50 g long-grain rice

2 leeks, washed and chopped

salt substitute (see page 14) and
    freshly ground black pepper

1/4 small cabbage, finely grated

1 tsp chopped parsley

NUTRITIONAL VALUES

1 Prepare the vegetables.

2 Heat the olive oil and toss the onion, celery, carrots and turnip in the saucepan. Stir over a low heat for about 4 minutes.

3 Add the water or stock to the vegetables. Then add the tomato purée, bouquet garni, bay leaf and mixed herbs. Bring to the boil. Add rice and simmer for 15 minutes.

4 Add the leeks and seasoning and continue cooking for a further 5 minutes.

5 Finally add the finely grated cabbage and cook for a further 5 minutes or until the rice is cooked. Toss in chopped parsley and serve.

CORN AND CHILLI CHOWDER

SERVES **3 – 4**

For those who like a little spice in their life. This recipe can be adjusted to how hot, or not so hot, you like your food.

1–2 fresh chillies

1 medium onion, finely chopped

2 tbsp olive oil

225 g canned or frozen sweetcorn kernels

600 ml low-fat milk

salt substitute and freshly ground black
  pepper

½ sweet red pepper, cored, deseeded
  and thinly sliced or finely diced
  (optional)

1 Split and deseed the chillies and soak them in cold salted water for an hour, changing the water occasionally. Rinse and chop finely.

2 Soften the chillies and the onion in the olive oil, then add the sweetcorn and cook for a minute more, stirring well.

3 Add the low-fat milk, cover, and simmer for 7 minutes.

4 Sieve, liquidize or process all, or only half, of the soup. It should not be too smooth.

5 Reheat, season and serve, garnished, if you like, with sweet red pepper.

NUTRITIONAL VALUES

MINTED PEA SOUP

SERVES **6**

Pea soup is one of the great classics. Use frozen peas, because peas straight from the pod never make it as far as the frying pan! Add just a little lime for an extra brightness of flavour, but the essential ingredients are young peas and fresh mint.

1 small onion, finely chopped

2 tbsp olive oil

450 g frozen peas

2 tbsp freshly chopped mint

1.1 litres water

grated rind of 1 lime

salt substitute (see page 14) and white pepper, to taste

low-fat fromage frais, to serve

1 Cook the onion slowly in the olive oil until soft but not brown; it is important to soften the onion really well as this soup has a very short cooking time. Stir in the peas and the mint, then add the water and bring the soup to the boil. Simmer for only 3–4 minutes, until the peas are just cooked; this will preserve the bright colour of the soup.

2 Cool the soup slightly then add the lime rind and purée until smooth in a blender or food processor. Rinse the pan and return the soup to it, seasoning to taste with salt substitute and white pepper. Reheat gently or allow to cool completely before chilling. Serve with a swirl of low-fat fromage frais.

NUTRITIONAL VALUES

CHICKEN AND BEAN SOUP

SERVES **6**

This is based on an Italian recipe for a tomato and bean soup. It is really a meal in itself when served with crusty bread.

2 tbsp olive oil

2 chicken thighs, skin removed

1 large onion, finely chopped

1 green pepper, deseeded and cut into strips

1 red chilli, deseeded and finely chopped

2 cloves garlic, crushed

1 tbsp freshly chopped oregano

1 tbsp freshly chopped flatleaf parsley

400 g chopped tomatoes

2 tbsp tomato purée

1.1 litre well-flavoured chicken or vegetable stock

salt substitute (see page 14) and freshly ground black pepper

425 g tin borlotti beans or mixed pulses, drained and rinsed

freshly chopped parsley and Parmesan cheese to garnish

NUTRITIONAL VALUES

1   Heat the oil in a large pan; add the chicken and brown all over. Remove the chicken from the pan with a slotted spoon and set aside. Stir the onion into the pan juices and cook until softened but not browned. Add the pepper, chilli and garlic with herbs and stir well. Add the tomatoes, tomato purée and stock then return the chicken to the pan, season lightly, and bring the soup to the boil. Cover and simmer for 40–50 minutes, until the chicken is cooked.

2   Remove the chicken from the pan and take the meat from the bones. Shred the chicken and return it to the pan with the beans. Return the soup to the boil, then simmer for 3–4 minutes to heat the beans thoroughly.

3   Season the soup to taste, then garnish with extra parsley. Slivers of Parmesan cheese may be sprinkled into the soup before serving.

CREAMY GARLIC MUSHROOMS

SERVES **4**

These are great as a starter, or equally good as a baked potato filler.

NUTRITIONAL VALUES

2 tbsp olive oil

1 large garlic clove, crushed

2 spring onions, chopped

salt substitute (see page 14) and freshly
   ground black pepper

750 g button mushrooms

112 g low-fat cream cheese

a little parsley, chopped (optional)

1 Heat the oil in a large frying pan. Add the garlic, onions and seasoning, and cook for 2 minutes. Then add all the mushrooms and toss them over high heat for a couple of minutes, until they are hot. Do not cook the mushrooms until their juices run as they will be too watery.

2 Make a clearing in the middle of the mushrooms, add the cream cheese and stir it for a few seconds, until it begins to soften. Gradually mix all the mushrooms with the cheese until they are evenly coated.

3 Divide among individual plates or dishes and top with a little chopped parsley, if liked. Serve at once with warmed wholemeal bread or toast.

4 Alternatively, transfer the mushrooms to a bowl, cool, then cover and chill them briefly before serving.

TOMATO AND SPRING ONION BRUSCHETTAS

These toasts have a scent of the Mediterranean about them, and the spring onions used here make a welcome change from the more typical garlic. Add mozzarella cheese if you wish, to make a more substantial snack.

2–3 ripe plum tomatoes

2 spring onions, finely sliced

salt substitute (see page 14) and freshly black
    pepper

2 tbsp olive oil

2 slices wholegrain bread

1 Slice the tomatoes and place them in a bowl with the spring onions. Season well, then add the oil and leave for 20 minutes, stirring from time to time.

2 Toast one side of the bread under a grill, then turn it over and pile on the tomatoes and spring onions. Reserve the olive oil. Grill until the tomatoes start to blacken – make sure all the bread is covered or it will burn.

3 Spoon the oil over the bruschettas and garnish with a small lettuce leaf or other greens to serve.

NUTRITIONAL VALUES

NUTTY CUCUMBER BOATS

SERVES **4**

A perfect first course for a hot summer day, or for a meal in the garden. You could add further texture and flavour – fibre too – by mixing three tablespoons of seedless raisins into the filling.

20 cm piece cucumber, cut in half lengthways

50 g pine kernels, toasted

25 g cashew nuts, toasted

125 g cottage cheese

4 medium tomatoes, skinned, deseeded and chopped

2 tsp chopped dill

1 tsp chopped mint

salad leaves

dill sprigs, to garnish

1 Scoop out the centres of the cucumber lengths and cut into 5 cm pieces.

2 Mix together the nuts, cheese, tomatoes, dill and mint. Spoon into each cucumber wedge.

3 Arrange the cucumber 'boats' on a bed of salad leaves, garnish with dill and serve at once.

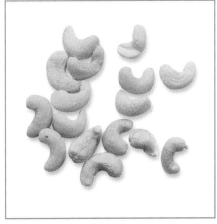

NUTRITIONAL VALUES

THREE PEPPERS IN TOMATO AND GARLIC

SERVES **4**

This is a summer tapa, and may be eaten hot or cold; its flavour improves after one day.

175 ml olive oil

2 yellow peppers, deseeded and cut into thin strips

2 red peppers, deseeded and cut into thin strips

2 green peppers, deseed and cut into thin strips

1 tbsp parsley, chopped

2 tsp garlic, crushed

225 g fresh or canned tomatoes

salt substitute (see page 14) and freshly ground black pepper

1 Heat the oil in a large frying pan and cook the peppers gently for 2–3 minutes, stirring frequently. Add the parsley and garlic and cook for another couple of minutes.

2 Add the chopped tomatoes and their juice to the pan. Stir and season.

3 Cover the pan and simmer gently for about 20 minutes, until the peppers are tender.

4 The sauce should be quite thick; if necessary, remove the peppers and boil rapidly to reduce the liquid. Check the seasoning.

5 If you like spicy seafood, substitute chilli oil for olive oil.

NUTRITIONAL VALUES

MUSSELS AND BEANS WITH TOMATO

SERVES **4**

Mussels have always been an excellent starter. For added flavour, complement them with bacon and tomatoes.

900 g haricot beans

3 tbsp olive oil

1 onion, chopped

2 slices good bacon, chopped

2 tsp garlic, crushed

825 ml chicken stock

900 g mussels, washed and debearded

1 beef (large) tomato, peeled and chopped

1 tbsp parsley, chopped

juice of 1 lemon

salt substitute (see page 14) and freshly ground
   black pepper

1   Soak the beans overnight in cold water, or buy ready-to-cook beans.

2   Heat the oil and sweat the onion in it until soft. Add the bacon and stir.

3   Add the beans and garlic, cover with the chicken stock and cook (20 minutes for canned beans, 2 hours for dried, soaked beans).

4   Add the mussels, shake, cover and cook until the mussels open.

5   Stir in the tomato, parsley and lemon juice. Season and serve in small bowls.

NUTRITIONAL VALUES

TURKISH ROASTED RED PEPPERS

SERVES **4**

A refreshing appetizer of roasted red pepper and yoghurt, this dish is rich with roasted aubergine and lightly spiced with cumin. It can be served as an accompaniment to chicken.

1 small to medium-sized aubergine, thickly sliced

salt substitute (see page 14)

5 tbsp extra virgin olive oil, or to taste

2–3 red peppers, roasted, peeled and diced

cayenne pepper to taste

4 cloves garlic, finely chopped

375 ml yoghurt

pinch cumin

juice of ½ lemon

fresh flat leaf parsley, to garnish

1 Generously sprinkle the aubergine with salt substitute and leave for at least 30 minutes. Rinse well and pat dry, then brown in about 2 tablespoons of olive oil, adding more if needed. Remove from the heat when the aubergine is tender and lightly browned, cut into small pieces.

2 Meanwhile, dice the roasted red peppers and toss them with the remaining olive oil, and salt substitute and cayenne pepper to taste. Mix the red peppers with the garlic and yoghurt, then stir in the aubergine, cumin and lemon juice. Taste for seasoning and chill until ready to serve. Garnish with flat leaf parsley.

NUTRITIONAL VALUES

AUBERGINE À LA GRECQUE

SERVES **4 – 6**

A marinated aubergine salad with mushrooms and chopped parsley. Serve with wholegrain bread to mop up the delicious juices.

1 large aubergine, sliced

125 ml olive oil

salt substitute (see page 14) and freshly ground
    black pepper

1–2 garlic cloves, minced

225 g white mushrooms, sliced

2–3 tbsp chopped fresh parsley

NUTRITIONAL VALUES

1   Preheat the grill. Arrange the aubergine slices in the pan and brush with olive oil. Grill until browned, turning occasionally.

2   Place the aubergine slices in a serving dish and add enough oil to moisten, but not so much that they are swimming in it. Season well, add the garlic, mushrooms and parsley and stir gently. Leave in the refrigerator for 1–2 hours then serve at room temperature for best flavour.

LETTUCE CUPS

SERVES **4**

A great way to enjoy the summer is with a refreshing meal. Use crisp Iceberg lettuce to really quench that summer heat.

4 tbsp long-grain brown rice

salt substitute (see page 14) and
   freshly ground black pepper

grated peel of ½ lemon

250 ml water

4 tbsp chopped walnuts

1 tbsp chopped fresh mint

2 tbsp chopped fresh parsley

1 tbsp olive oil

a little lemon juice

4 Iceberg or Romaine lettuce
   leaves

4 tomatoes skinned, if liked, and
   diced

2 spring onions, chopped

1 Place the rice in a small frying pan with a sprinkling of salt substitute and lemon peel. Pour in the water and bring to the boil. Stir once, reduce the heat and cover the pan. Cook the rice gently for 25 minutes, or until only just tender. Leave the lid on the pan, removed from the heat, for 5 minutes, by which time the rice should be tender and dry.

2 Add the walnuts, mint, parsley, oil and lemon juice to the hot rice, then fork the ingredients into the grains until well mixed. Cover and leave to cool.

3 Place a lettuce leaf on each serving plate. Divide the rice mixture among the lettuce cups, spooning it into a ring shape on each. Mix the tomatoes and spring onions and pile the mixture in the middle of the rice rings.

4 Serve with warm, crusty wholegrain bread.

NUTRITIONAL VALUES

MUSHROOM AND HERB PASTA SALAD

SERVES **4 – 8**

Any small pasta shapes can be used in this dish. It can be served as a main course for lunch, or as a side dish for cold meats.

300 g dried pasta shapes

dash of olive oil

225 g cup mushrooms, quartered

1 red pepper, cored, deseeded and cut into squares

225 g pitted black olives

4 tbsp fresh basil, minced

2 tbsp fresh parsley, minced

DRESSING

2 tsp red wine vinegar

1 tsp salt substitute (see page 14)

freshly ground black pepper

4 tbsp extra virgin olive oil

1 garlic clove, minced

1–2 tsp Dijon-style mustard

1 Bring a large frying pan of water to a boil, and add the pasta and a dash of olive oil. Cook for about 10 minutes, until tender. Drain and rinse under cold running water. Drain well again.

2 Place the cooked pasta in a large salad bowl, and add the remaining ingredients. Toss together to combine.

3 To make the dressing, place all the ingredients in a bottle and shake well. Pour the dressing over the salad and toss together. Cover and refrigerate for at least 30 minutes, then toss again before serving.

NUTRITIONAL VALUES

MIMOSA BEANS

SERVES **4**

This dish is bound to impress, with its amazing flavour and eye-catching appearance.

450 g French or green beans, trimmed and halved

1 tsp fresh sage, chopped

1 tbsp fresh parsley, chopped

2 hard-boiled eggs, shelled

1 tbsp lemon juice

salt substitute (see page 14) and freshly ground
   black pepper

150 ml low-fat natural yoghurt

1 Place the beans in a frying pan with 6 tablespoons water, the sage and the parsley.

2 Cover and simmer gently for 10 minutes, until the beans are tender but still crisp.

3 Meanwhile cut one egg in half, then cut two slices and reserve. Separate the white from the yolk of the cut egg and the remaining whole eggs.

4 Chop the white finely and sieve the yolk. Drain the beans, add the lemon juice, seasoning and yoghurt.

5 Arrange the beans on a warmed serving plate spreading out from the centre.

6 Decorate the centre with the reserved egg slice. Place the egg white in a ring around the yolk and serve.

7 If wished this dish may be served cold as a salad. Leave the beans and yoghurt to cool before decorating with the egg.

NUTRITIONAL VALUES

MAIN COURSES

PAELLA DE VERDURAS CON PESTO DE NUECES

SERVES **6**

The combination of earthy walnut pesto with delicate, saffron-infused rice is simply magical. Chopped walnuts can be sprinkled on top of the paella to further enhance the nutty flavour of the rice.

FOR THE WALNUT PESTO

50 g fresh basil leaves, finely chopped

3 tbsp chopped walnuts

3 tbsp grated Manchego or Parmesan cheese

4 cloves garlic, finely chopped

4 tbsp olive oil

2 tbsp walnut oil

FOR THE PAELLA

575 ml chicken broth

175 ml dry white wine

½ tsp saffron

4 tbsp olive oil

1 small onion, finely chopped

1 medium red pepper, finely chopped

125 g oyster mushrooms, destemmed and chopped

125 g shiitake mushrooms, destemmed and chopped

2 medium courgettes, chopped

2 medium tomatoes, finely chopped

8 artichoke hearts, quartered

2 tbsp chopped parsley

½ tsp sweet paprika

350 g long-grain rice

chopped walnuts, to garnish

NUTRITIONAL VALUES

1 First, make the walnut pesto. Place the basil leaves, chopped walnuts, grated cheese and garlic in a food processor and blend until paste forms. With the motor still running, add the olive oil and walnut oil little by little, until well incorporated. Set the pesto aside.

2 Combine the chicken broth, white wine and saffron in a frying pan over low heat. Keep heated until ready for use.

3 To make the paella, heat the olive oil in a paella pan and sauté the onion and red pepper over medium heat for several minutes. Mix in the mushrooms, courgettes, tomatoes, artichokes, parsley and paprika, and cook for several minutes longer.

4 Pour the rice, and combine well. Stir in the broth mixture and pesto sauce and continue to cook until the liquid has been absorbed and the rice is tender. Serve warm and, if desired, sprinkled with chopped walnuts.

STUFFED PEPPERS

SERVES **4**

The stuffing is so good and versatile that it can be used to stuff aubergine and courgette.

4 assorted coloured peppers

75 g instant couscous

6 spring onions, trimmed and chopped

50 g raisins

1 tbsp grated lemon rind

¼–1 tsp dried crushed chillies, according to taste

2 tomatoes, deseeded and chopped

50 g strong-flavoured cheese, such as Cheddar
   cheese, grated

2 tbsp toasted pine kernels

1 tbsp chopped freshly ground black pepper

1 large egg, beaten

150 ml vegetable stock

flatleaf parsley, to garnish (optional)

1 Pre-heat a slow cooker on high. Cut the peppers either in half lengthways or cut off the tops to form a lid. Remove and discard the seeds and membrane, then cover with boiling water and leave for 5 minutes, drain and reserve.

2 Meanwhile place the couscous in a bowl, cover with boiling water and leave until all the water has been absorbed. Add the chopped spring onions, raisins, lemon rind, chillies, tomatoes, cheese, pine kernels, parsley and seasoning to taste. Mix well, then bind together with the beaten egg. Use to stuff the peppers, then place in the cooking pot.

3 Heat the stock and pour around the peppers, cover with the lid and cook on high for 2–4 hours. Serve, if like, garnished with flat-leaf parsley.

NUTRITIONAL VALUES

WARM BEAN AND PUMPKIN SALAD

SERVES **6**

The spinach cooks so quickly that it is added right at the very end of the cooking time. You could use frozen spinach, but fresh is definitely better. For a change, use Swiss chard in place of the spinach.

125 g dried haricot beans, soaked overnight

125 g dried red kidney beans, soaked overnight

125 g dried black-eye beans, soaked overnight

2 tbsp olive oil

1 large onion, peeled and cut into wedges

small pieces fresh root ginger, peeled and grated

2–4 garlic cloves, peeled and chopped

¼–1 tsp dried crushed chillies

1 tsp cumin seeds

1 tsp ground coriander

½ tsp turmeric

450 g pumpkin, peeled, deseeded and diced

300 ml vegetable stock

125 g cherry tomatoes, quartered

175 g spinach, thoroughly washed and grated

175 g feta cheese, diced

fresh coriander sprigs

salt substitute (see page 14) and freshly ground
   black pepper

low-fat natural yoghurt and warm pitta bread strips,
   to serve

1 Cover the beans with cold water and leave to soak overnight. Next day, drain, place in a pan and cover with water. Bring to the boil and boil for 10 minutes. Drain and reserve.

2 Preheat a slow cooker on high. Heat the oil in a frying pan and sauté the onion with ginger, garlic, chillies to taste and all the spices for 3 minutes. Add the pumpkin and continue to sauté for 3 more minutes, then spoon into the cooking pot and stir in the drained beans. Heat the stock to boiling and pour over the vegetables and beans. Cover, reduce temperature to low then cook for 8–10 hours.

3 Just before serving, stir in the tomatoes and spinach, stir well and continue to cook for 15–20 minutes or until the spinach has begun to wilt. Sprinkle with the diced feta cheese and freshly chopped coriander and serve with low-fat natural yoghurt and strips of warm pitta bread.

NUTRITIONAL VALUES

ROASTED RATATOUILLE WITH TOFU

SERVES **4**

This oven-roasted ratatouille is tossed in a tangy vinaigrette of balsamic vinegar and olive oil.

1 each red, yellow and orange pepper, deseeded
   and cut into chunks

125 g chestnut mushrooms, cut into quarters

1 green courgette, sliced into rounds

1 yellow courgette, sliced into rounds

1 aubergine, cut into chunks

4 plum tomatoes, cut into quarters lengthways

250 g firm tofu, cubed

5 tbsp extra-virgin olive oil

ground black pepper

2 tbsp balsamic vinegar

1 tbsp fennel seeds

basil leaves, to garnish

1   Preheat the oven to 200°C/gas mark 6.

2   Spread out the peppers, mushrooms, courgettes, aubergine, tomatoes and tofu in a shallow roasting tin. Sprinkle with the olive oil and season with plenty of freshly ground black pepper.

3   Turn the vegetables and tofu over so that they are coated in oil and roast for 30–40 minutes or until the vegetables are tender and scorched at the edges. When they are cooked, transfer to a serving dish, sprinkle with the vinegar and fennel seeds and serve at once, garnished with basil leaves.

NUTRITIONAL VALUES

ONION RAVIOLI

This is a rich and delicious pasta dish. Serve it as a main course with a simple side-salad, or divide into smaller portions and serve as an appetizer.

2 large onions

4 tbsp olive oil

1 clove garlic, finely chopped

large pinch ground mace

freshly ground black pepper

12 fresh no-cook lasagne noodles

75 g chopped walnuts

125 ml olive oil

1–2 tbsp shredded sorrel

NUTRITIONAL VALUES

1 Chop one and a half of the onions, then cook them in 2 tablespoons olive oil with the garlic and mace until soft and golden brown – about 10 minutes over medium heat. Add the pepper then allow to cool.

2 Dampen the edges and crossways along the middle of each sheet of lasagne, one at a time. Place about 1 teaspoon of onions on one end of each noodle, then fold the lasagne over in half and seal the edges to make a ravioli pouch. Leave on a damp tea towel until ready to cook.

3 Slice the remaining onion and cook it in the pan until golden with any remaining onion filling. Once browned, add the chopped walnuts and the olive oil. Heat until the oil gets warm.

4 Bring a large pan of water to a boil. Add the ravioli and cook gently for 3–4 minutes, then drain and add to the sauce with the shredded sorrel. Season to taste and serve.

FUSILLI WITH SUN-DRIED TOMATOES

A dish that is delicious served warm as a main course or cold as a summer salad. Tomato pesto is widely available.

450 g dried fusilli (twists)

dash of olive oil, plus extra for drizzling

2 tbsp tomato pesto

175 g sun-dried tomatoes, drained and chopped

4 plum tomatoes, sliced into wedges

4 tbsp chopped fresh basil

freshly ground black pepper

NUTRITIONAL VALUES

1 Bring a large frying pan of water to the boil and add the fusilli with a dash of olive oil. Cook for about 10 minutes, stirring occasionally, until tender. Drain and return to the frying pan.

2 Stir in the remaining ingredients, drizzle with olive oil and serve warm immediately, or cool and refrigerate to serve chilled if preferred.

WHOLEMEAL LASAGNE WITH MEDITERRANEAN VEGETABLES

SERVES **4**

Mediterranean cooking is very healthy. With its vast array of sun-ripened vegetables, delicious pastas, breads and rich unctuous oils, it is easy to see why. This recipe captures all the richness of the ingredients.

3 tbsp olive oil

1 onion, peeled and chopped

3 garlic cloves, crushed

6 sun-dried tomatoes, chopped

250 g aubergine, chopped

1 yellow pepper, deseeded and chopped

2 courgettes, chopped

150 ml puréed tomatoes

150 ml red wine

salt substitute (see page 14) and freshly ground
    black pepper

1 tbsp chopped fresh oregano

6–8 fresh wholemeal lasagne sheets

4 firm tomatoes, sliced

50 g grated mozzarella cheese

extra chopped fresh oregano

NUTRITIONAL VALUES

1 Preheat the oven to 190°C/gas mark 5, 10 minutes before baking the lasagne. Heat the oil in a frying pan and sauté the onion, garlic and sun-dried tomatoes for 5 minutes. Add the aubergine, yellow and red peppers and courgettes and continue to sauté for 3 minutes.

2 Stir in the puréed tomatoes, wine, seasoning to taste and the oregano. Bring to the boil, reduce the heat, and simmer for 15 minutes or until the vegetables are almost cooked.

3 Bring a large pan of water to the boil, add 1 tablespoon salt, then drop in 4 lasagne sheets, one at a time. Cook for 2–3 minutes, ensuring that they do not stick together. Drain, lay them on clean tea-towels, and pat dry. Repeat with the remaining lasagne sheets.

4 Place a layer of the vegetable sauce in the base of an ovenproof dish and top with half the lasagne sheets. Cover with the remaining sauce and then the lasagne sheets.

5 Arrange the tomato slices on top and sprinkle with the grated cheese. Bake in the oven for 25 minutes or until the cheese is golden and brown. Serve sprinkled with chopped oregano.

SMOKED HADDOCK KEDGEREE

SERVES **4**

A relatively simple dish which is packed with flavour. Can be served as a main course, or divided into smaller portions for appetizers.

1 onion, finely chopped

2 tbsp olive oil

175 g long-grain brown rice

550 ml water

175 g haddock

1 hard-boiled egg, chopped

salt substitute (see page 14) and cayenne pepper

¼ tsp grated nutmeg

1 tbsp lemon juice

2 tbsp fresh parsley, chopped

lemon and lime wedges, to garnish

4 slices wholegrain toast, cut into triangles, to serve

1 Place the onion and olive oil in a large frying pan and cook over a medium heat for 2–3 minutes. Add the rice, stir well and cook for 1 minute, stirring continuously.

2 Add the water, cover and simmer gently for about 30 minutes, or until the water is absorbed and the rice is tender.

3 Meanwhile place the haddock in a large pan barely covered with water. Simmer for 7–10 minutes or until the fish flakes easily when tested with the point of a knife.

4 Drain, skin and flake the fish discarding any bones. Add to the cooked rice with the egg, seasoning, nutmeg and lemon juice. Stir gently over a moderate heat for 3–4 minutes.

5 Place the kedgeree on a warm serving dish, sprinkle with the parsley and garnish with lemon or lime wedges. Serve with wholemeal toast triangles.

NUTRITIONAL VALUES

GRILLED JUMBO PRAWNS

Prawns are a rich source of protein and minerals but are low in calories, making them a perfect ingredient for healthy dishes. With the rice, olives and oilve oil, this recipe has an authentic Mediterranean taste.

1 onion, finely chopped

250 g long-grain rice

3 Tbsp olive oil

675 g raw jumbo shrimp or large prawns in their
  shells

olive oil for brushing

salt substitute (see page 14) and freshly ground
  black pepper

about 2–3 tbsp chopped parsley

SAUCE

1 onion, chopped

1 garlic clove, chopped

1½ tbsp oil

565 g well-flavoured tomatoes, deseeded and
  chopped

1 bouquet garni

150 ml medium-bodied dry white wine

12 oil-cured pitted black olives

1 To make the sauce, cook the onion and garlic in the oil until softened but not coloured. Stir in the tomatoes and cook for a few minutes before adding the bouquet garni, wine, and olives. Simmer gently until it as thickened.

2 Meanwhile, cook the onion and rice in the olive oil, stirring, until golden. Add water to cover generously and bring to the boil. Then cover the pan and simmer for about 12 minutes until tender.

3 Preheat the grill.

4 Thread the prawns on skewers, brush with oil, and grill for 7–8 minutes, turning occasionally.

5 Drain the rice, rinse quickly with boiling water and stir in the parsley and seasoning.

6 Season the sauce and discard the bouquet garni. Serve the prawns on a bed of rice, accompanied by the sauce.

NUTRITIONAL VALUES

FISH AND VEGETABLE CASSEROLE

SERVES **8-10**

Cod, haddock or monkfish would all be suitable types of fish to use for this dish, which originates from the Greek island of Corfu. The crucial ingredient is the garlic, and plenty of it.

6 tbsp olive oil

1 large onion, sliced

900 g small new potatoes, washed and cut into
   1.25 cm slices

2 carrots, cut into 2.5 cm chunks

1 celery stick, chopped

salt substitute (see page 14) and freshly ground
   black pepper, to taste

6 garlic cloves, crushed

1.2 kg firm white fish fillets, skinned and cut into 5
   cm chunks

62 ml freshly squeezed lemon juice

NUTRITIONAL VALUES

1 Heat ½ cup of the olive oil in a large, heavy-based saucepan and sauté the onion for about 3 minutes, or until softened.

2 Add the potatoes, carrots and celery, and season with salt and freshly ground black pepper. Continue to cook for about a further 4–5 minutes, or until the vegetables begin to soften.

3 Stir in the garlic and pour over enough boiling water to just cover the vegetables. Bring to a boil, cover and simmer for about 10–15 minutes or until the vegetables are almost tender.

4 Gently stir the fish into the casserole, cover and simmer for 10–15 minutes or until the fish flakes easily, adding a little extra water if necessary. Just before the end of the cooking time, remove the cover, and stir in the lemon juice and the remaining olive oil. Adjust the seasoning if necessary and serve.

MUNG BEAN AND PASTA SALAD

SERVES **4**

For a vegetarian salad, omit chicken and prawns. Add 300 g of washed, finely chopped mushrooms.

125 g mung beans, cooked

125 g wholemeal pasta rings, cooked

4 spring onions, washed

125 g cooked chicken (optional)

125 g sweetcorn, cooked

125 g cooked prawns (optional)

300 ml low-fat mayonnaise or yoghurt dressing

TO GARNISH

2 spring onions, chopped

2 tomatoes, sliced

¹/₂ lettuce, washed

1 Mix all the ingredients in a bowl with the dressing.

2 Arrange the tomatoes and lettuce leaves around a bowl. Pile in the salad and garnish with chopped spring onions.

NUTRITIONAL VALUES

SCALLOP, PRAWNS AND SAFFRON RICE

SERVES **4**

It is preferable to use saffron strands rather than saffron powder. Either soak the strands in warm water for a few minutes, then use both the strands and soaking liquor, or sprinkle straight into the dish at the beginning of cooking.

2 tbsp olive oil

1 onion, peeled and chopped

2 medium leeks, trimmed and sliced

few saffron strands

175 g easy-cook brown long-grain rice, rinsed

275 g scallops, rinsed and halved if large

225 g large uncooked, peeled prawns

600 ml fish or chicken stock

1 orange pepper, peeled and chopped

4 tomatoes, deseeded and chopped

salt substitute (see page 14) and freshly ground
  black pepper

2 tbsp chopped fresh parsley

2 medium eggs, hard-boiled, shelled and
  quartered, to garnish

1 Preheat the cooker on high. Wipe the cooking pot with a little of the olive oil, then heat the remaining olive oil in the frying pan and sauté the onion and leeks for 3 minutes, stirring frequently. Add the saffron and rice and continue to sauté for 2 minutes. Add the scallops and prawns and cook for 3 minutes, stirring, then add the remaining ingredients except for the parsley and eggs and bring to the boil.

2 Spoon into the cooking pot, cover with the lid and cook for 2–3 hours. Stir, adjust the seasoning, then serve immediately, sprinkled wih the parsley and garnished with the hard-boiled eggs.

NUTRITIONAL VALUES

FISHERMAN'S PIE

This tasty and warming main course can be served on its own, with vegetables or with salad.

675 g potatoes, cubed

425 ml milk

2 tbsp olive oil

salt substitute (see page 14) and freshly ground
  black pepper

1 onion, chopped

125 g button mushrooms, sliced

40 g plain flour

175 g frozen peas

125 g frozen sweetcorn

2 tsp fresh dill, chopped

2 tsp fresh parsley, chopped

400 g can tuna chunks in brine, drained

1 tbsp Parmesan cheese, shredded

fresh herbs, to ganish

1 Place the potatoes in a large shallow dish and add 6 tablespoons water. Cover with pierced microwave film and microwave on high for 11–12 minutes, or until tender.

2 Drain and cream together with 25 ml milk, 1 tablespoon oil, and seasoning.

3 Place the remaining oil in a large casserole dish and microwave on high for 40–50 seconds to melt. Add the onions and mushrooms and microwave on high for 2 minutes.

4 Stir in the flour then gradually stir in the milk. Microwave on high for 4 minutes, or until thickened, stirring 2–3 times during cooking.

5 Stir in the peas, sweetcorn, dill, parsley and tuna. Cover and microwave on high for 5 minutes.

6 Place in a shallow heatproof dish, pipe or fork the potato on top and sprinkle with Parmesan cheese. Microwave on high for 4–5 minutes. Place under a preheated grill to brown.

7 Garnish with herbs and serve.

NUTRITIONAL VALUES

DIFFERENT FISH PIE

This quick, and extremely tasty, fish dish is quite a departure from the traditional combination of fish in white sauce with mashed potato topping.

1 kg potatoes

salt substitute (see page 14) and freshly ground
    black pepper

675 g white fish fillet

grated peel and juice of ¹/₂ lemon

2 tbsp olive oil

1 onion, chopped

1 tsp dried marjoram or oregano

1 garlic clove, crushed (optional)

450 g sliced mushrooms

2 x 400 g cans chopped tomatoes

2 tbsp chopped fresh parsley

75 g grated cheddar cheese

NUTRITIONAL VALUES

1 Cut the potatoes into thick slices, then into fingers (or French fry shapes) and across into large dice. Place them in a large saucepan, add water to cover, and a little salt substitute. Put over a medium heat, until the water is just boiling.

2 Meanwhile, lay the fish on a large plate or dish to go on top of the saucepan of potatoes. Sprinkle with a little seasoning, and the lemon peel and juice. Cover the fish with a second plate, lid or foil and put it on top of the potatoes when they are boiling. Reduce the heat, if necessary, so the water is just boiling and cook for about 10 minutes, or until the potato dice are tender. Remove the fish but leave it covered on the plate. Drain the potatoes well.

3 While the potatoes are cooking, heat the oil in a frying pan or flameproof casserole. Add the onion, marjoram or oregano and garlic, if used, and cook gently for about 20 minutes, until the onion is soft and well cooked.

4 Add the mushrooms to the onion and fry them for about 5 minutes before pouring in the tomatoes. Stir well, add a little seasoning and bring to the boil. Reduce the heat and let the mixture simmer gently while you remove the skin and any bones from the fish.

5 Pour the juices from the fish into the tomato mixture, then flake the flesh (it should not be well cooked yet) into fairly large chunks. Discard the skin and all bones, then lightly stir the fish into the tomato mixture. Simmer for about 5 minutes, until the fish is cooked and hot. Taste for seasoning and stir in the parsley.

6 Turn the fish mixture into a dish to go under the grill. Top with the potatoes, then sprinkle with the cheese. Place under a moderately hot grill until the cheese has melted and the potato topping is crisp and golden. Serve at once.

AUBERGINE AND COD BAKE

SERVES **4**

A simple bake with the flavours of the Mediterranean. Serve this with a crisp green salad and crusty French bread to mop up the juices.

olive oil

1 aubergine, sliced

1 large onion, finely sliced

1 garlic clove, crushed

2 tbsp capers

30 g black pitted olives, Provençal if possible

300 g chopped tomatoes

1 tbsp chopped mixed fresh herbs, such as
   parsley, oregano, marjoram

salt substitute (see page 14) and freshly ground
   black pepper

4 x 175 g pieces of thick cod fillet, skinned

NUTRITIONAL VALUES

1   Preheat the oven to 200°C/gas mark 6. Lightly oil an 20 cm round ovenproof serving dish.

2   Heat 2–3 tablespoons of oil in a large frying pan and fry the aubergine slices gently until tender but not brown. Drain on kitchen towels. Add a little more oil if necessary, then add the onion and cook until softened and just starting to brown. Stir in the garlic, capers and olives, then add the tomatoes, herbs and seasoning to taste. Simmer the sauce for about 5 minutes, until it is slightly thickened and the onions are cooked.

3   Pour the sauce into the prepared dish, then nestle the cod fillets into it. Cover the fish with the aubergine slices. Place the dish on a baking tray if it seems very full and likely to bubble over, then bake in the hot oven for 20 minutes, until the aubergine slices are browned. Serve immediately.

OATY MACKEREL

A simple, delicious variation on traditional herrings in oats.

8 tbsp medium steel-cut oats

salt substitute (see page 14) and freshly ground
   black pepper

4 small mackerel, gutted with heads off and boned

a little lemon juice

1 Put the oats on a plate and season well. Hold one mackerel by its tail and sprinkle the flesh side with a little lemon juice. Press the fish on the oats, flesh down and use a spoon to dust more oats over the top of the fish. Press the oats on well then lay the mackerel on a grill tray. Repeat with the remaining mackerel.

2 Cook the mackerel under a moderately hot grill, allowing about 10 minutes on each side, until the oats are browned and crisp and the fish is cooked through.

3 Serve piping hot, with thin crusty bread.

NUTRITIONAL VALUES

BAKED CODLING PROVENÇAL

SERVES **4**

A well-presented whole fish creates a tremendous impression at a dinner party, especially when it is surrounded by a colourful and piquant sauce. You can cook other fish such as grey or red mullet in a similar way.

1 small codling, about 1.125 kg, cleaned, washed and dried

2 tbsp wholemeal flour

3 tbsp sunflower oil

FOR THE SAUCE

400 g can chopped tomatoes

2 medium onions, finely chopped

125 g mushrooms, chopped

150 ml red wine

1 tbsp chopped parsley

2 tbsp pine kernels

12 black olives

pepper

1 Rub the fish on both sides with the flour. Heat the oil in a large frying pan and fry the fish over medium heat for about 6–7 minutes on each side, or until it is tender when pierced with a fine skewer or knife.

2 Meanwhile put the tomatoes (with juice), onions, mushrooms and wine into a small pan, bring to the boil and simmer, stirring frequently, for about 15 minutes, until the sauce has thickened. Stir in the parsley, pine kernels and olives and season with pepper.

3 Place the fish on a heated serving dish and pour the sauce around it. Serve with small new potatoes boiled in their skins, or with wholemeal noodles.

NUTRITIONAL VALUES

QUICK CHICKEN RISOTTO

SERVES **4**

A little cooked chicken and a selection of colourful vegetables with rice makes an appetizing and filling dish which can be served with a green or tomato salad.

225 g basmati rice, washed and drained

600 ml chicken or vegetable stock

1 medium onion, sliced

1 clove garlic, crushed

4 tender celery sticks, thinly sliced

1 small green pepper, deseeded, cored and
   chopped

1 small red pepper, deseeded, cored and chopped

125 g canned sweetcorn kernels, drained

50 g seedless raisins

225 g boneless chicken, cooked

1 tbsp soy sauce

pepper

2 tbsp chopped walnuts

2 tbsp chopped parsley

1 Put the rice and stock into a large, shallow pan, bring to the boil, cover and simmer gently for 15 minutes, when most of the stock should have been absorbed.

2 Stir in the onion, garlic, celery, peppers and sweetcorn and continue to cook for 10 minutes.

3 Stir in the raisins, chicken and soy sauce and season with pepper. Allow just to heat through, then stir in the walnuts and parsley. Sprinkle with chopped parsley to serve.

NUTRITIONAL VALUES

BLUSHING CHICKEN LIVERS

Here the chicken livers are cooked quickly in a spicy tomato sauce. They are good served with jacket potatoes, new potatoes or noodles and a green salad.

450 g chicken livers

2 Tsp olive oil

1 tbsp vegetable oil

1 large onion, diced

1 clove garlic, crushed

½ tsp hot chilli powder

3 tomatoes, peeled, deseeded and sliced

2 tbsp tomato purée

125 ml red wine or Marsala

½ tsp thyme, freshly chopped

pinch ground bay leaves

1 tsp Worcestershire sauce

salt substitute (see page 14) and freshly ground
    black pepper

150 ml low-fat fromage frais

freshly chopped parsley, to garnish

1 Rinse the chicken livers and pat dry on kitchen towel.

2 Heat the oil in a saucepan. Sauté the onions and garlic until lightly browned and softened.

3 Sprinkle in the chilli powder and stir in the chicken livers. Cook for 4 minutes.

4 Add the tomatoes and mushrooms and cook for a further minute. Then stir in the tomato purée, red wine or Marsala, herbs and Worcestershire sauce. Simmer, uncovered for 4 minutes. The liquid will reduce a little.

5 Season to taste and stir in the fromage frais.

6 Serve immediately, garnished liberally with chopped parsley.

NUTRITIONAL VALUES

PAPRIKA CHICKEN

SERVES **4**

Paprika chicken uses, as the name implies, the subtle, milder dried red pepper – never to be confused with or substituted for hotter members of the family like cayenne or chilli. Serve this warming dish with noodles or pasta shells.

1.6 kg oven-ready chicken

2 tbsp olive oil

2 medium onions, peeled and thinly sliced

2 tsp paprika

125 ml dry white wine

450 g tomatoes, deseeded and chopped

1 tbsp tomato purée

2 whole pimentos (sweet red pepper), chopped
   roughly

bouquet garni

4 tbsp low-fat natural yoghurt

1 tbsp chopped parsley

1   Joint the chicken into 8 pieces, and remove the skin where possible.

2   Heat the oil in a large pan and sauté the chicken until browned. Remove and set aside. Add the onions to the pan and cook until softened.

3   Sprinkle in the paprika and cook for a further minute. Blend in the wine.

4   Return the chicken pieces to the pan together with the tomatoes, purée, pimentos and bouquet garni. Cover and simmer for 45 minutes.

5   Transfer the chicken to a serving dish to keep warm. Rub the contents of the pan through a sieve. Return to rinsed pan and reheat. Season to taste.

6   Swirl in the yoghurt and pour over the chicken pieces. Sprinkle with the chopped parsley. Serve immediately.

NUTRITIONAL VALUES

CORIANDER CHICKEN WITH PILAU RICE

SERVES **4**

Fresh coriander has a unique, pungent flavour.

1 tbsp olive oil

8 chicken thighs

1 large onion, sliced

1 tbsp paprika

1 tsp ground cumin

1 tbsp turmeric

½ tsp dried thyme

freshly ground black pepper

300 ml well-flavoured chicken stock

25 g pitted black olives

2 tbsp fresh coriander, finely chopped

squeeze of lemon juice

PILAU RICE

2 tbsp vegetable oil

50 g whole blanched almonds, toasted

1 small onion, finely diced

50 g sultanas or raisins

350 g long-grain rice

750 ml boiling water

½ tsp salt substitute (see page 14)

NUTRITIONAL VALUES

1 Heat the oil in a large pan and fry the chicken until an even, rich brown. Transfer to a plate.

2 Add the onion to the remaining oil and cook until softened and golden. Stir in the paprika, cumin and turmeric and cook for a further minute. Add the thyme, black pepper and stock and bring to the boil.

3 Return the chicken to the pan, skin side down. Cover and simmer for 1 to 1¼ hours or until the chicken is tender.

4 Remove the chicken with a slotted spoon to a heated serving dish and keep warm.

5 Reduce the sauce by rapidly boiling until it thickens. Stir in the olives, coriander and lemon juice. Season to taste and pour over the chicken.

6 For the rice, heat the oil in a large pan and cook the onion until softened but not coloured. Add the toasted almonds, sultanas and rice, and cook for a further minute, stirring thoroughly.

7 Add the boiling water and salt. Bring to the boil, then cover and reduce the heat to simmer. Cook for 15 minutes, or until all the water has been absorbed and the rice is tender, but still firm. Fork the rice lightly and serve with the chicken.

SPAGHETTI WITH CHICKEN LIVERS

SERVES **4**

For a twist on a traditional meal use chicken livers, which have a fantastic texture, and red peppers for a sweet taste.

450 g chicken livers, diced

1 red pepper, deseeded

1 clove garlic, crushed

2 tbsp olive oil

salt substitute (see page 14) and freshly ground
  black pepper

4 tomatoes, skinned and chopped

2 basil leaves, chopped

450 g spaghetti

oil

freshly chopped parsley (optional)

NUTRITIONAL VALUES

1 Prepare the chicken livers by cutting into small pieces.

2 Cut and dice the pepper finely. Blanch it for 2 minutes in water that has just boiled and drain. Crush the garlic.

3 Heat the olive oil in a frying pan and simmer the garlic and pepper for 5 minutes.

4 Add the chicken livers and stir round, mixing with the pepper. Cook for 5 minutes on a low heat. Add the tomatoes, basil and seasoning.

5 While the sauce is simmering cook the spaghetti in boiling water with a few drops of oil. Drain and mix well with the chicken liver sauce. Each portion can be garnished with some freshly chopped parsley.

CARIBBEAN CHICKEN WITH WARM FRUIT SALSA

SERVES **4**

Salsas are very popular and can be made using many different ingredients. The chilli here gives a pleasant, fiery tang. Use as much of the chilli as your palate can take.

FOR THE MARINADE

4 skinless chicken breasts

2 cloves garlic, crushed

½ to 1 habanero chilli, deseeded and finely chopped

1 tbsp grated lime zest

2 tbsp grated root ginger

3 tbsp fresh lime juice

125 ml mango or orange juice

2 tbsp chopped coriander

1 tbsp olive oil

chopped fresh coriander and lime wedges

FOR THE SALSA

1 firm but ripe papaya, peeled and deseeded

1 small fresh pineapple peeled and sliced, or 2–3 slices fresh pineapple

2 firm tomatoes, deseeded and chopped

4 spring onions (white and green parts), trimmed and finely chopped

2 tbsp chopped coriander

NUTRITIONAL VALUES

1. Make three slashes diagonally across each chicken breast and place in a glass baking dish.

2. For the marinade, combine the garlic, chilli, lime zest and ginger in a bowl. Stir in the fruit juices and coriander. Pour over the chicken and coat all sides. Cover and marinate in the refrigerator for 30 minutes, stirring occasionally.

3. For the salsa, slice the papaya thickly. Brush the fruit and rack with olive oil. Grill over a medium heat until seared on each side. Remove, chop finely, and mix with the remaining salsa ingredients.

4. Drain the chicken for the marinade. Grill over medium heat, 5–6 minutes per side. Serve garnished with coriander and lime wedges on top of 1–2 spoonfuls of warm salsa.

SMOKED CHICKEN BREAST SANDWICH

SERVES **8**

Succulent chicken pieces, served in delicious Italian bread.

FOR THE MARINADE

50 ml fresh lemon juice

50 ml balsamic vinegar

4 cloves garlic, crushed

1 tsp dried oregano

1 tsp black pepper

1 tsp grated lemon rind

50 ml virgin olive oil

8 150 g boneless, skinless
   chicken breasts

450 ml boiling water

75 to 125 g sun-dried
   tomatoes, not packed in oil

one 50 cm loaf

Italian pesto

1 small packet rocket leaves,
   washed and dried

1   Combine the lemon juice, vinegar, garlic, oregano, black pepper and grated lemon rind in a bowl and beat in the oil with a wire whisk until well blended. Place the chicken breasts in a zip-lock plastic bag or a non-reactive baking tin. Pour the marinade over the chicken, cover and marinate for 2–4 hours in the refrigerator.

2   Remove the chicken breasts from the marinade and place on the rack in the pan smoker. Add wood chips and heat until the chips start to smoke. Cover with the lid and smoke for about 30 minutes or until cooked.

3   In a heatproof bowl pour the boiling water over the tomatoes, cover, and leave to stand for 20–0 minutes or until soft. Drain the tomatoes and pat dry.

4   Cut the loaf of bread in half horizontally and spread with basil olive pesto. Slice the chicken breasts and place on the bottom half of the loaf, top with tomatoes and arugula, cover with the top of the loaf and secure with cocktail sticks.

NUTRITIONAL VALUES

QUICK HAM AND BEAN CASSEROLE

SERVES **4**

Shoyu is a fermented soya bean product. It is quite salty, so there is no need for additional seasoning.

450 g new potatoes, scrubbed

1 tbsp sunflower oil

1 onion, chopped

275 g cooked red kidney beans or 400 g can red
  kidney beans, drained

450 g whole-kernel corn

175 g ham, cubed

400 g chopped tomatoes

2 tbsp tomato purée

2 tbsp Worcestershire sauce

1 tbsp shoyu sauce

tabasco, to taste

freshly ground black pepper

onion rings, to garnish

wholemeal pitta bread, to serve

1 Place the potatoes in a saucepan of lightly salted boiling water and cook for 15 minutes, or until just tender. Drain and dice.

2 Place the oil and onion in a large pan and cook for 2–3 minutes to soften.

3 Add the potatoes, kidney beans, sweetcorn, ham, tomatoes with their juice, tomato purée, Worcestershire sauce, shoyu, tabasco and seasoning to taste. Place in a warmed casserole dish and garnish with onion rings.

4 Serve with wholemeal bread if wished.

NUTRITIONAL VALUES

SPICED MINCED BEEF AND LENTIL CUTLETS

SERVES **4**

Vary the quantity of chillies to suit your taste. If you find that your mixture is too soft to form cutlets, don't worry; use a spoon to drop it into the pan and it will thicken as it cooks.

150 g red lentils

500 g minced beef

1 medium onion, chopped

2 green chillies, sliced

5 cm piece fresh root ginger, peeled and sliced

3 bay leaves

4 cloves

8 black peppercorns

¼ tsp cardamom seeds, or 6 pods

½ tsp coriander seeds

5 cm stick cinnamon

1 tsp chopped fresh coriander

2 egg yolks

TO GARNISH

sliced tomatoes, onion rings, cream coconut
   shavings, fresh coriander leaves

1   In a non-stick pan cook the lentils in plenty of water for 40 minutes and then dry them out to a paste by stirring constantly to prevent them from burning on the base of the pan. Allow to cool.

2   In a saucepan mix the beef with the onions, chillies, ginger, bay leaves, cloves, peppercorns, cardamom, coriander seeds and cinnamon in 600 ml water. Season and simmer for 40 minutes until dry but do not allow to brown. Cool a little then purée in a food processor. Add the lentils, coriander, and egg yolks and blend again for a further 30 seconds to a smooth thick paste. Check the seasoning and chill.

3   Form the mixture into cutlets and fry in a little hot oil until brown on both sides. Serve garnished with sliced tomatoes, raw onion rings, shavings of creamed coconut and fresh coriander leaves.

NUTRITIONAL VALUES

LAMB WITH LENTILS AND PRUNES

SERVES **4**

This casserole has many of the classic flavours of southwest France: plump, moist prunes, green lentils and fresh thyme. The lentils and prunes make it a filling dish and mean that much less meat is required per person than in a more traditional casserole.

2 tbsp olive oil

4 lamb chops or leg steaks, or 450 g lamb fillet, cut into 4 pieces

1 large onion, sliced

3 sticks celery, sliced

2 large carrots, sliced

2 plump cloves garlic, sliced finely

1 tbsp fine wholemeal flour

450 ml well-flavoured vegetable or lamb stock

200 g prunes

100 g green lentils

6 juniper berries, lightly crushed

4–5 sprigs fresh thyme

freshly ground black pepper

1 Preheat the oven to 160°C/gas mark 3. Heat the oil in a flameproof casserole dish and brown the lamb on all sides. Remove the meat with a slotted spoon and set aside until needed. Add the onion to the casserole and cook slowly until softened but not browned, then add the celery, carrot and garlic and continue cooking for a further 2 to 3 minutes.

2 Stir the flour into the vegetables and cook for 1 to 2 minutes, then gradually add the stock, stirring to scrape up any sediment from the bottom of the pan. Bring to the boil; add the prunes and lentils and simmer for 2 to 3 minutes. Return the lamb to the casserole and add the remaining seasonings. Cover, then cook in the preheated oven for 1½–2 hours. Season to taste before serving the lamb on a bed of the vegetables with the sauce spooned over.

NUTRITIONAL VALUES

DESSERTS

TROPICAL FRUIT SALAD

A refreshing pudding, that can be made with a variety of fruits.

225 g mango flesh

175 g honeydew melon

125 g kiwi fruit

150 g lychees, canned

2 tbsp orange juice

2 tbsp lemon juice

1 tbsp artificial sugar

NUTRITIONAL VALUES

1 Cut the mango into bite-size cubes.

2 Use a melon baller to cut out as many little balls as possible from the melon.

3 Peel and slice the kiwi fruit.

4 Drain the lychees.

5 Mix the orange and lemon juice and sugar together and pour this over the fruit. Mix well and chill.

6 Just before serving, divide the fruit among 4 serving dishes and top each one with whole lychees.

YOGHURT DELIGHT

SERVES **4**

The delicious sweetness of honey and fruits, combined with the textures of the nuts and the smoothness of the yoghurt, makes this a delightful pudding.

175 g low-fat yogurt

grated zest and juice of 1 orange

50–125 ml clear honey

drop of oil

25 g shelled pistachio nuts

25 g Brazil nuts, roughly chopped

25 g raisins

2 firm pears, peeled, cored and diced

40 g ready-to-eat dried apricots, sliced

25 g seedless grapes, halved

1 Mix the yoghurt, orange zest, and 2–3 tablespoons of the honey, then divide it among 4 dishes and chill well.

2 Warm the oil, then stir fry the pistachios and Brazils with the raisins for 3 minutes. Add the pears and continue to stir fry for about 3 minutes, or until the pears are lightly cooked. Stir in the apricots and orange juice and bring to the boil. Boil, stirring, for 2 minutes to reduce the orange juice.

3 Stir in the grapes and remaining honey (or to taste) and heat through briefly. Spoon the fruit and nut mixture on top of the chilled yoghurt and serve at once.

NUTRITIONAL VALUES

BLACKBERRY OATIE

SERVES **4**

This dessert has its origins in Scotland, where the combination of oats and whisky strikes a chord of national pride.

50 g rolled porridge oats

5 tbsp whisky

3 tbsp clear honey

125 g low-fat curd cheese

150 ml plain low-fat yoghurt

1 tbsp grated orange rind

225 g dessert blackberries, hulled

fresh mint, to garnish

NUTRITIONAL VALUES

1 Put the oats and whisky into a bowl, cover and set aside for at least 2 hours, or overnight if it is more convenient.

2 Beat together the honey, cheese and yoghurt and stir in the orange rind. Stir in most of the blackberries.

3 In 4 tall glass dishes, make layers of the fruit mixture and oats beginning and ending with the fruit. Decorate each glass with a few reserved berries and a sprig of fresh mint. Serve chilled.

PEACH AND ALMOND CRUMBLE

SERVES **4 – 6**

Crumbles are always a family favourite, and one of the best and most healthy accompaniments is low-fat yoghurt. This one is made in a slow cooker, and is the perfect end to any meal.

6 ripe fresh peaches, skinned, stoned and sliced,

5 tbsp peach or orange juice, optional

1 tbsp honey, optional

½ tsp almond essence

125 g wholemeal flour

50 g porridgeoats

25 g ground blanched almonds

50 g demerara sugar

1 tsp ground cinnamon

8 tbsp peanut butter

2 tbsp toasted flaked almonds

mint sprigs, to garnish

frozen low-fat yoghurt to serve

1 Preheat a slow cooker on high. Using a 1.5 litre heatproof dish, arrange the sliced fresh peaches in the base or drain the canned peaches, reserving 4 tablespoons of their juice, and place the canned peaches in the base.

2 If using fresh peaches, pour over the peach or orange juice and honey. If using canned fruit, use the canned juice. Sprinkle the fresh or canned peaches with the almond essence.

3 Place the flour, oatmeal, almonds, sugar and cinnamon into a bowl, add the peanut butter and blend in. Sprinkle over the peaches and pat down lightly. Cover with the lid, then reduce the temperature to low and cook for 4–5 hours. Remove from the cooker, and sprinkle with the flaked almonds, garnish with mint sprigs, and serve with frozen low-fat yoghurt.

NUTRITIONAL VALUES

MINCEMEAT AND APPLE TART

SERVES **6**

Mincemeat is full of fibre from the dried fruits that it contains. The apples help to take away much of the richness of the mincemeat, and mixing the pastry with a little orange rind and juice also helps.

5–6 tbsp olive oil

175 g fine wholemeal flour

grated rind and juice of
  1 orange

FOR THE FILLING

350 g mincemeat

1–2 red-skinned dessert apples,
  cored and sliced

juice of 1 lemon

2 tbsp honey

1 Preheat the oven to 190°C/gas mark 5. Blend the olive oil into the flour, then stir in the orange rind. Bind the pastry together with the orange juice, then roll it out and use to line a 20 cm cake or flan tin.

2 Spread the mincemeat evenly in the pastry case then arrange the sliced apples around the edge, brushing them with lemon juice. Bake the tart in the preheated oven for 30–35 minutes.

3 Brush the apples carefully with honey as soon as the tart is removed from the oven, then leave to cool slightly before serving.

NUTRITIONAL VALUES

FRUIT SALAD

SERVES **4**

*This is a refreshing pudding for summer evenings. It is much healthier – and tastier –
than those purchased from the supermarket.*

2 medium–sized juicy oranges

2 limes

25 g raspberries

25 g golden raspberries

25 g strawberries

25 g blueberries

25 g blackberries

1 large papaya

2 kiwi fruit, peeled and sliced

20 g fresh coconut meat, grated or scant 25 g
  desiccated coconut

1   With a knife, remove all the skin from the
oranges. Holding the oranges over a medium bowl
to catch the juices, cut along the membranes of
the oranges so the segments fall into the bowl as
well. Repeat the process for the limes.

2   Add the raspberries, strawberries, blueberries and
blackberries. Cover and refrigerate for 2 hours.

3   Peel the papaya, cut in half, and remove the seeds.
Cut each half into 1 cm slices and arrange on 4
plates with the sliced kiwi fruit.

4   Spoon the berry and orange mixture, with the
juices, over the papaya. Sprinkle with coconut.

NUTRITIONAL VALUES

BANANA CUSTARD

SERVES **3 – 4**

Bananas are a great source of vitamins, and can help keep you fighting fit. This is a super little pudding to increase your fruit intake.

2 bananas, sliced

grated rind and juice of 1 lemon

450 g low-fat yogurt

75 g pecans, chopped roughly

1 tbsp honey

75 g bran

whole milk

1 Toss the banana slices in lemon juice, then place in a bowl. Carefully mix in the yoghurt, nuts, honey and bran. If the mixture is very thick, add 1 or 2 tablespoons of milk to thin it out.

2 Decorate with lemon rind just before serving.

NUTRITIONAL VALUES

HAZELNUT AND APRICOT CRUNCH

MAKES **16**

These tasty oat bars are a healthy dessert, and they also make a good breakfast.

8 tbsp olive oil

50 g soft brown sugar

2 tbsp maple syrup

125 g porridge oats

50 g chopped hazlenuts

50 g dried apricots, chopped

1   Preheat the oven to 180°C/gas mark 4.

2   Put the butter, sugar and syrup in a heavy pan and stir over a low heat until combined.

3   Stir in the remaining ingredients. Press into a Swiss roll pan lined with greaseproof paper. Bake for about 45 minutes, until golden. Cut into bars in the pan using an oiled knife. Cool in the tin.

NUTRITIONAL VALUES

APPLE AND CARROT CAKE

MAKES **16 SLICES**

This is a moist, well-flavoured and very successful dessert.

250 g self-raising wholemeal flour

125 ml olive oil

1 tsp cinnamon

150 g chopped walnuts

100 g raisins

300 g peeled, cored, and grated dessert apples

150 g grated carrot

grated peel of 1 orange

2 large eggs

4 tbsp fresh orange juice

NUTRITIONAL VALUES

1 Line the base and grease a loaf tin with 500 ml capacity.

2 Preheat the oven at 180°C/gas mark 4.

3 Place the flour in a bowl and mix well, then cut in the olive oil and stir in the cinnamon. Stir in the walnuts, raisins, apples and carrot. Add the orange peel, eggs and juice, then beat well until thoroughly combined.

4 Spoon the mixture into the prepared tin, smooth the top and bake for about 1¼ hours, or until the cake is well risen and firm to the touch. Turn out and cool on a wire rack.

BLUEBERRY CHEESECAKE

SERVES **2**

Cheesecake with a delicious muesli and dried fig base, in place of the usual crushed biscuits and butter, which gives a rich and crunchy base to the soft filling.

225 g plain muesli

150 g dried figs

1 tsp vegetarian gelatine

4 tbsp cold water

125 ml skimmed evaporated milk

1 egg

6 tbsp caster sugar

450 g low-fat cottage cheese

125 g blueberries

50 g blueberries

2 nectarines, stoned and sliced

2 tbsp honey

1 Place the muesli and dried figs in a food processor and blend together for 30 seconds. Press into the base of a base-lined 8 in spring release tin and chill while preparing the filling.

2 Sprinkle the gelatin onto 4 tablespoonfuls of cold water. Stir until dissolved and heat to boiling point. Boil for 2 minutes. Cool. Place the milk, egg, sugar and cheese in a food processor and blend until smooth. Stir in the blueberries. Place in a mixing bowl and gradually stir in the dissolved gelatin. Pour the mixture on to the base and chill for 2 hours until set.

3 Remove the cheesecake from the tin and arrange the fruit for the topping on top. Drizzle the honey over the fruit and serve.

NUTRITIONAL VALUES

BRAN FRUIT LOAF

MAKES **900g LOAF**

Because of the sugar, treacle and honey content of this loaf, view this as a special treat to be enjoyed occasionally and only after a low-GI main course.

50 g bran cereal

300 ml skimmed milk

225 g self-raising wholemeal flour

1 tsp baking powder

1 tsp salt substitute (see page 14)

125 g seedless raisins

50 g currants

50 g sultanas

75 g dark muscovado sugar

2 tbsp clear honey

2 tbsp black treacle

oil, for brushing

1   Soak the cereal in the milk for 30 minutes.

2   Set the oven to 180°C/gas mark 4. Sift together the flour, baking powder and salt substitute and stir into the cereal mixture, together with any bran remaining in the sieve. Stir in the raisins, currants, sultanas, sugar, honey and treacle and mix well.

3   Lightly brush a 900 g loaf tin with oil. Spoon in the cake mixture and level the top. Bake in the oven for 1–1¼ hours, or until the loaf is well-cooked and a skewer inserted in the centre comes out clean.

4   Allow the loaf to cool slightly in the tin, then turn it out to cool on a wire rack. When it is completely cool, wrap it in foil and store it in an airtight tin.

NUTRITIONAL VALUES

OATCAKES

MAKES **16**

These oatcakes are delicious eaten with fruit and cheese.

225 g medium grain oatmeal

¼ tsp salt

¼ tsp bicarbonate of soda

2 tbsp olive oil

6–7 tbsp water

NUTRITIONAL VALUES

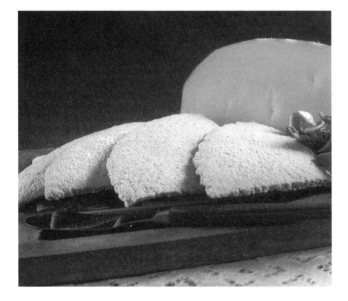

1 Preheat the oven to 160°C/gas mark 3.

2 Pour the oatmeal into a bowl with the salt and bicarbonate of soda.

3 If using the griddle to cook, preheat. (If using a non-stick frying pan, it will take less time to heat than the griddle). Make sure the temperature is right as it is better to work quickly with oatcakes once they are started.

4 Heat the olive oil. Add to the oatmeal mix and gradually pour in enough hot water to make a stiff dough – the water must be added gradually so that the dough does not become too sticky.

5 Turn on to a work surface sprinkled with oatmeal and knead well. Divide the dough into pieces. Sprinkle the work surface with oatmeal again and make each piece into a neat round, roll out to approximately 0.75 cm sandwich cake tin or plate. Cut into four or eight triangles.

6 Cook over a medium heat for about 3–4 minutes or until the edge of the oatcake begins to curl. Remove and rub the smooth side with more oatmeal.

7 Reheat in a moderate oven for a few minutes before serving. If serving straight away, oatcakes can be placed under the broiler for a few minutes to become golden. However, if using the broiler, do take care otherwise the oatcakes will burn easily.

8 Alternatively, cut the oatcakes in rounds with a pastry cutter and cook on the griddle or in the oven for about 30 minutes. Allow to cool on a wire tray and store in an airtight container.

INDEX